LESSONS IN PROFESSIONAL LIABILITY

DPIC's Loss Prevention Handbook for Design Professionals

Edited by Sheila A. Dixon

Different by Design®

The Professional Liability
Specialist of the
Orion Capital Companies

DPIC Companies, Inc.
P.O. Box DPIC
2959 Monterey-Salinas Highway
Monterey, California 93940
800/227-4284

ISBN 0-932056-07-5
Library of Congress Catalog Card Number 94-072300

Acknowledgments

This edition of *Lessons in Professional Liability* is truly the work of many individuals. In the late 1970s, Edward B. Howell and Richard P. Howell published their groundbreaking work in loss prevention for design professionals, *Untangling the Web of Professional Liability*. The first edition of *Lessons*, edited by Alison Edwards and published in 1988, was an updated version of that book. This new edition draws on the first two books as well as the guidance of several people, all of whom deserve our thanks.

Architects Bruce Sellery, AIA-E, and Larry Segrue, FAIA and engineer Paul Carroccio, P.E., L.S., FASCE (who is now with DPIC) gave us their valuable review and comment. Susan Tsantiris, Esq., of Orion Capital Companies law division, provided a thoughtful in-house legal review.

At DPIC Companies, Senior Vice President Russ Chaney oversaw and championed the project, while Claims Senior Vice President Elliott Gleason offered his critique, and patiently answered queries about dispute resolution and claims. Loss Prevention/Marketing Manager Tag Wilson and Vice President Pat Marshall, Professional Liability Agents Network Liaison officer, also painstakingly reviewed the manuscript. Most especially, thanks go to Senior Vice President Dick Crowell, co-author of DPIC's *The Contract Guide* and loss prevention guru, who invested a great deal of his time and expertise in this edition.

Cris Dawson, of Dawson Design, created the design of the book and Editor Ruth Menmuir lent her extraordinary skills. The DPIC Communications staff — Manager Paula Crisler, Editor Tom Owens, Administrator Mary Cooke, and Desktop Publishing Supervisor Dorothy Doudy — undertook the final editing and production of the book.

The late Peter Hawes, DPIC's president, CEO and guiding light, also contributed his thoughts to this edition. It is our hope that his high standards and unflagging belief in DPIC — its people, policyholders, and purpose — are reflected herein.

The Editor

Notice to Readers

This publication is intended to provide accurate and authoritative information about the subject matter covered. It is not to be regarded as providing opinion or advice for any individual case. This publication is sold and distributed with the understanding that the publisher is not engaged in rendering legal or other professional service. If legal advice or other expert assistance is required, the services of a competent professional person should be sought.

(IV)

TABLE OF CONTENTS

Chapter Four - Business Practices   61

Chapter Five - Technical Procedures   125

List of Exhibits

INTRODUCTION

It has been almost fifteen years since DPIC published its first loss prevention manual, *Untangling the Web of Professional Liability*, and almost seven years since its successor, the first edition of *Lessons in Professional Liability*, was printed. During those years, unfortunately, we have seen little improvement in the liability crisis that confronts the construction industry. Architects and engineers still face the very real threat of claims on every project they undertake. The sad truth is that any claim can prove disastrous for a design practice. Given the small profit margin of the typical firm, a single claim can mean the difference between profit and loss on a project; a large claim can spell bankruptcy.

This is why it is so important for design professionals to understand how to avoid litigation. Unfortunately, engineering and architectural students don't learn much in classrooms about the real world problems of unintended liability for jobsite safety, delay claims by contractors and onerous contract clauses by client attorneys. But these are just the sort of situations design professionals will confront every day.

Loss prevention must become a necessary part of design practice. In fact, design professionals today are expected to be much more than architects and engineers. As the CEO of a large engineering firm put it: "They'll be part lawyer (to deal with liability and other legal issues); part doctor (to contend with health and safety concerns); part computer scientist (to utilize advanced automation); part business administrator (to manage capital investments in new technologies); part social worker (to anticipate the cultural impacts of their work); and part educator (to inform society of the important role they play)."[1]

Is it all really worth it? One design professional wrote us recently to ask, "With all the liability involved in being a professional, why would anyone want to be in practice?" Surely doctors and other professionals ask themselves the same question. After all, surgeons don't go through medical school so they can wade through piles of red tape and earn huge malpractice suits for their trouble. The answer is not to abandon the practice but to extend the education. Architects and engineers spend years studying the design of buildings or roads, dams and landscapes — but probably not one day learning how to negotiate a well-worded, protective contract.

But such a contract does not come about by accident. It is the end product of a realistic process that begins by asking design professionals to take a hard look at the way they do business. If you recognize how your everyday business practices can affect your exposure to litigation, you really can affect the odds that you will be sued. In fact, DPIC was founded on this very principle. We believe that once you've learned to identify, weigh and manage the risks you face, you can practice your chosen profession with greater confidence.

First, you must identify your risks. Learn to honestly assess a potential client, the type of project, your capabilities, your consultants, your contract, your workscope and your fees. Once identified, risks can be managed in a number of ways.

Some risks you just accept as part of your everyday practice. This does not mean that you are powerless to control them. You can reduce some exposure by offering more comprehensive services and by developing a clear and reasonable contract. In addition, you need to learn to spot those practices in your day-to-day work that result in claims against design professionals, and manage them with proven loss prevention techniques.

You can also transfer some of your risk by means of professional liability insurance. But insurance won't completely protect you. There are also ways to apportion risk to those better equipped to handle it — the client and the contractor — by using limitations of liability and indemnifications that you can negotiate in your agreement with your client.

Finally, some risks are so substantial that no amount of insurance or contractual protection would make them worth the potential loss. These risks should simply be avoided altogether by declining the project.

We've put together this updated edition of our manual on loss prevention to help you get started learning how to lower your exposure to claims. After you have read it carefully, it is our hope that you will have a basic understanding of why claims occur, and the best methods to prevent or mitigate those claims.

Although technical competence and experience are discussed, it is not the purpose of this manual to educate you in the technical areas of your profession. Instead, it is intended to raise your awareness of how certain actions can lead to professional liability claims.

We begin by discussing professionalism. Unless you thoroughly understand your duties and responsibilities as a licensed professional, you can jeopardize your practice through increased exposure to risk.

Next, we discuss professional communication. Faulty communication is often at the root of many design professional disputes. Very often a claim can be traced back to a misunderstanding by either the design professional or the client about what the other party expected.

We describe some worthwhile techniques you can use to avoid disputes. We explain how to confront, manage and resolve a conflict should it arise, addressing both formal dispute resolution techniques and litigation.

We then examine how business procedures can either reduce or increase your exposure to professional liability claims. We show you how to identify and evaluate the risks of a project, how to select your clients and how to improve your chances of collecting your fees. We analyze the provisions in a professional services contract that will get you and your firm into trouble, and identify the risks in preparing cost estimates and scheduling your services. Finally, we touch on the relationships between prime consultants and subconsultants, and on the management of human resources.

We identify the technical areas of a design professional's practice that are the most persistent sources of professional liability claims. We discuss the liability pitfalls in the design, bidding and construction phases of a project.

Although all of the practices described above reduce exposure, losses cannot be completely eliminated. Professional liability insurance is your last line of defense. We discuss how to select a good insurance broker, what to expect from a professional liability insurer and how to read and understand your policy.

Finally, to help you find more information on specific topics, we identify a number of resources and include a list of reference materials.

Remember, the advice from any book is worthwhile only if it is implemented. Your diligent loss prevention and business management efforts can reduce damaging claims and create more profitable operations, too.

[1]James W. Poirot, past president of ACEC and chairman of the board of CH2M Hill Companies, Ltd.

PROFESSIONALISM

What does it mean to be a professional today? Historically, the mark of a professional has been the mastery and use of a specialized body of knowledge. In antiquity, it was the tribal religious leader; later it was the barber (a specialist in surgical matters); and in relatively recent times it has been the family doctor, the minister, the lawyer. Now it is also the architect and engineer. Yet the meaning of professional has stayed essentially the same; only the body of knowledge has mushroomed and the movement from knowledge to application has become more structured, more complex. Under standards ensured by the profession, your knowledge has been acquired through a rigorous and specialized education, applied in internships, tested in comprehensive examinations and certified through licensure. You and your colleagues have earned — and society acknowledges — the right to practice your profession.

With this right comes certain obligations to both the public and your profession. You are charged with the responsibility to protect public health, safety and welfare and to put society's needs before your own. You are expected to uphold the integrity of your profession and to contribute, through experience and research, to the base of knowledge from which other members will draw.

With greater responsibility comes greater risk. There is a standard of care to which you and other members of your profession are expected to perform. Society requires that those who are providing professional services will do so in a reasonably careful and prudent manner, as tested or established by the actions of their own peers under similar circumstances. Although you do not have to be perfect (at least the law doesn't require it; your client may have different ideas), you are expected to uphold the professional standard of practice or face legal sanctions.

A Professional Practice

It takes more than an education in engineering or architecture to be a design professional. The word *professional* also connotes the skills you bring to your practice. To serve society and your clients — and to survive in today's competitive market — you need two separate sets of skills. You must have both *technical* and *business* expertise.

First, of course, you must have the basic *technical competency* that is acquired through formal education and internships. Over the years, you are expected to build on that foundation by keeping current with developments in your discipline.

There's more to a successful design practice than producing superior plans and specifications, however. Before the advent of universities, an aspiring novice learned from close daily contact with an established professional. The professional oversaw almost every aspect of the student's life, conduct and goals, cultivating professional qualities by daily example and instruction. This sort of relationship is virtually nonexistent in the modern world. Today, individual courses required for a technical degree are taught by people who are experts in those courses. Relationships between practicing professionals and students are more distant. As a result, most university education processes can provide only the technical ABCs.

Yet a design student needs to understand the conditions of his or her chosen profession and its real opportunities and responsibilities. Architects and engineers must be able to analyze, evaluate, choose and compete. Today's designs are judged not only on appearance or function but also on feasibility of construction and life cycle cost. Design professionals must understand, in the words of one architect, "*how things get built.*"

3

Second, no matter how creative or talented you may be, you also need a thorough grounding in *business skills* in order to function professionally in the real world. Clients are becoming increasingly sophisticated. Many are highly experienced in building projects; others have degrees in business or law. Then, too, many projects involve collaboration among a variety of specialists, increasing the need for sophisticated project management. To stay competitive, architects and engineers must be able to respond to their clients' higher expectations and to handle the demands of working effectively with many other parties. They must hone their communications skills in order to market their services and lessen their risk exposure. They need to learn the basics of financial management, contract formation and negotiation, human resources management and insurance management. They also need to learn to anticipate and then resolve the disputes that will surely arise.

In short, today's design professionals must devote the same level of energy and attention to the business side of their practice as they do to the preparation of plans and specifications. If you doubt the importance of this, understand that many professional liability claims stem from the *non-technical* aspects of a design practice, such as acceptance of onerous contract terms and conditions, poor communication, careless selection of projects, failure to record all significant decisions and lax fee-collection practices.

A Professional Public Image

Over the last few decades there has been a growing mistrust in institutions, government and authority figures in general. Without a doubt, this suspicion extends to some of the professions. While almost everyone has a doctor and many have an accountant, the average citizen may never use the services of a design professional and, therefore, has little knowledge of the discipline. Because of this, many people base their opinions about design professionals on what they read in newspapers or see on television — and that publicity has not always been favorable. Headlines about the rare but spectacular building failure are what people remember.

Many people have no idea what it is design professionals do for a living. There may be a vague understanding that architects build buildings, whatever that means. As for engineers, well, nobody really knows what engineers do, besides drive trains.

But does it really matter that John and Jane Q. Public don't appreciate the subtleties of your profession? The answer is a resounding *Yes!* This lack of understanding makes you and every other design professional more vulnerable to claims from clients as well as the public. If people don't know what you do, then they also don't know what you *don't* do. They may believe, for instance, that you are responsible for the accident at the jobsite or that you personally tested the roofing system for the new school.

It falls to each architect and engineer to enhance public understanding of his or her profession. People base their ideas of your profession on their perception of your actions. Hence, the technical and aesthetic competence you show, coupled with an environmental sensibility, a fairness of judgment and a good sense of public purpose and duty, will help them define the profession as well as your place in the profession.

You can go a step further by working to educate the public. Take an active role in your community. There are so few architects and engineers in public office that it is little wonder that the needs of those professions are often not met. Run for the school board, or the city council; offer to serve on your town's planning commission. As a professional, you can provide valuable expertise to your community — and teach others about your job.

The better you tell your story, the better you serve your profession. If you explain the merits of project partnering (see page 36), qualifications based selection (see page 77) or limitation of liability (see page 95) at a Rotary or Chamber of Commerce luncheon, someone important (perhaps a future client or the city attorney) might hear you. If you tell a career day assembly full of high school students about what a geotechnical engineer does, some of those kids might take an interest in science and math. In a few years, one of them may work for a client or may even become an employee in your firm. If you write or, better yet, visit your congressperson or state assembly members to urge action on legislation that will help your profession, you might just be heard. If 50 colleagues from your local district do the same, someone in government is going to sit up and take notice.

As you work to educate the public about the value and role of your discipline, you may be pleasantly surprised to find that such an effort is an effective marketing tool. Even more important, you will be helping to reduce professional liability claims against design professionals and taking steps to shore up the erosion of public confidence in the professions.

Professional Conduct and Ethics

Most people do not know that design professionals have rules of professional conduct and codes of ethics they must follow and that violation of these rules is grounds for disciplinary action. The rules of professional conduct are primarily enforced by each state, whose designated administrative agency has the power to admonish, censure and revoke or suspend the license to practice in that state. These rules of conduct, in fact, are important reasons design professionals have earned the right to be called professionals. In addition, professional societies develop and enforce their own standards of ethical behavior. Violations of these rules of conduct can also result in admonition, censure, suspension or termination of membership. As a reminder, we reprint the ACEC's *Fundamental Canons* and AIA's *Code of Ethics and Conduct Canons*. (See *Exhibits 1* and *2*.)

Post a copy of your professional association's code of ethics in your office and remind your employees that they are expected to abide by it. There is no clearer way of emphasizing to your clients — and to your employees — that you believe in maintaining those levels of conduct.

Exhibit 1 ACEC's Fundamental Canons

**ACEC's Professional and Ethical Conduct Guidelines
Fundamental Canons**

Consulting engineers, in the fulfillment of their
professional duties, shall:

1. Hold paramount the safety, health and welfare of
    the public in the performance of their professional duties

2. Perform services only in areas of their competence

3. Issue public statements only in an objective and
    truthful manner

4. Act in professional matters for each client as faithful
    agents or trustees

5. Avoid improper solicitation of professional assignments

Reprinted by permission from the American Consulting Engineers Council

Exhibit 2 AIA's Code of Ethics and Conduct Canons

The American Institute of Architects Code of Ethics and Professional Conduct, 1987

Canon I: General Obligations

Members should maintain and advance their knowledge of the art and science of architecture, respect the body of architectural accomplishment and contribute to its growth. Learned and uncompromised professional judgment should take precedence over any other motive in the pursuit of the art and science of architecture.

Canon II: Obligations to the Public

Members should embrace the spirit and letter of the law governing their professional affairs and should thoughtfully consider the social and environmental impact of their professional activities.

Canon III: Obligations to the Client

Members should serve their clients competently and in a professional manner, and should exercise unprejudiced and unbiased judgment when performing all professional services.

Canon IV: Obligations to the Profession

Members should uphold the integrity and dignity of the profession.

Canon V: Obligations to Colleagues

Members should respect the rights and acknowledge the professional aspirations and contributions of their colleagues.

Reprinted by permission from the American Institute of Architects

Summary

- As a professional, you have earned the right to practice your profession. Along with this right, however, comes certain obligations to society, including the duty to protect public health, safety and welfare.

- As a professional, you also are expected to perform to a certain standard of care and to uphold the standards of your profession.

- To compete in today's market and to avoid claims, you need to master skills in business as well as maintain technical competency.

- Many claims against design professionals stem from the non-technical aspects of a design practice.

- It is important that the public learn more about the design professions. Each architect and engineer has the ability — and responsibility — to enhance his or her profession.

- Design professionals have rules of professional conduct and codes of ethics that they are required to follow. Noncompliance is grounds for disciplinary action by the state licensing agency and/or the architect's or engineer's professional society.

Metred.

0   5   10   20   30   40   5

b

F

G   G

E

COMMUNICATIONS

No matter how much you might wish you could work alone on a new design, you do not have that luxury. Today's construction projects can be extremely complex, often requiring the input of dozens of specialists, all of whom must communicate with each other. You must interact daily with diverse personalities in order to develop clients, present proposals, listen to subconsultants, deal with public officials, respond to contractors and resolve inevitable conflicts. In this sue-first-ask-questions-later world of ours, the truth is that any or all of these personalities can be the source of a claim against you.

A large number of claims made against design professionals result not simply from technical errors or incompetence but from a breakdown in understanding between parties — either in the written communication of the project itself (the contract documents) or in the day-to-day communications between you and other parties to the construction process.

This need not happen. You can anticipate and deal with many of these problems by considering the factors that lead to misunderstandings between the design professional and other members of the construction team.

The Importance of Communications

Effective verbal and written communication does not come naturally for most people. Some who are adept at the spoken word — politicians, for example — may have trouble writing a clear, concise letter. Others, such as literary scholars, can write a beautifully constructed manuscript, yet have difficulty in communicating the same ideas in speech.

Some colleges and universities do little to help fledgling design professionals in these areas. While an exhaustive background in mathematics, physics and other technical subjects is provided, only a few courses in the humanities or business are required. In fact, a student can graduate from most accredited schools of architecture or engineering without taking more than a few courses outside his or her own field of study. It sometimes seems that the schools assume their students will acquire, by some magical process, skill in communications and interpersonal relationships.

To further complicate matters, people often feel they understand one another perfectly, when, in reality, they do not. They are operating in what psychologists call "pseudo-communication." They use the same words and phrases but each interprets them differently depending upon his or her own background. National origin, gender, culture, education and past experiences all play a role in the "understanding" reached.

The Words We Use

As we've noted, communication failures often are at the center of lawsuits. A primary culprit is the language we use in our written communication, including correspondence, specifications and contractual agreements.

No matter what you intended to say, when such a claim arises, the courts are called upon to decide what the language communicated, based on case law. Attorneys, in building their cases, frequently refer to a special dictionary of words and phrases that lists interpretations by the courts.[1] For instance, regardless of your interpretation of the word *inspection*, the plaintiff's attorney may argue that there is no reason to debate the meaning of the word, saying, "It was decided in the case of State Farm Mutual v. Rickhoff that it means '...to examine carefully or critically, investigate and test officially, especially a critical investigation or scrutiny.'"

If you guess that the dictionary providing this definition is a single volume, be prepared for a shock. The dictionary is made up of scores of volumes of about 700 pages each — roughly 70,000 pages in all!

A look at this dictionary reveals that some words seem to be misunderstood far more often than others. Take, for example, the word *final*. Interpretations of this word fill more than 500 pages. Clearly, it is a word best avoided in your communications. In fact, if we categorize words that take up significant space in this dictionary, we find they fall into several groups:

- Extreme words, such as *final, all, complete* or *best*
- Words of multiple meaning, such as *inspect* or *estimate*
- Words of promise, such as *guarantee* or *certify*.

Have you been asked to sign an agreement with a clause such as the following?

> *The Design Professional shall assist the Owner in applying for and obtaining from ALL applicable public agencies, ANY permits, approvals or waivers required by law.*

If you've seen a clause like this, your clue to possible trouble is the frequent use of extreme words. It is important to try to delete or change them. Often, you will find that the owner does not intend to impose the impossible conditions that such words imply and would not object to your modifying the clauses.

Take a closer look at the preceding clause. As it reads now, you could be held responsible for obtaining every conceivable permit necessary for others to do their work. It establishes an absolute condition that may be impossible for you to meet. You can't know at the beginning of a project what permits might be required, but if you accept such a clause, you are agreeing to an open-ended requirement for any new approvals that might be imposed in the future. Instead, you could modify the clause to read:

> *The Design Professional shall assist the Client in applying for those permits and approvals typically required by law for projects similar to the one for which the Design Professional's services are being engaged. This assistance consists of completing and submitting forms required for the performance of certain work included in the Scope of Services.*

Most of us tend to use extreme words. For example, we frequently agree to *maximize, minimize* or *optimize* without thinking twice. We often employ words of totality such as *any, all, none, full* or *equal* without qualification in our brochures, contracts or proposals.

In addition to extreme words, words that have multiple meanings cause innumerable problems for the design professional. Simple little words sometimes have dozens of meanings. Look up the words *run, top* and *get* in your desktop dictionary. Seeing the variations of meaning for these three-letter words might make it easier for you to believe that the 500 most commonly used words in the English language have more than 14,000 meanings!

Inspect and *supervise* are two words that mean something different to design professionals than to lay persons. In fact, the word *supervise* should probably be avoided — or used with extreme caution — by design professionals. Note how a jury might conclude that *supervise* is synonymous with *control* from the following definitions in *Words and Phrases:*

> The words *supervise, superintend* and *oversee* in ordinary use and common acceptance have substantially the same meaning.

> *Control* is the "power or authority to manage, direct, superintend, restrict, regulate, govern, administer or oversee."

> The terms *direct* and *administer* are synonymous. Both mean "to manage, control and conduct affairs of business."

Clearly, these definitions overlap; at least 10 words are listed as synonymous with *supervise*. For a design professional, this is treacherous ground. In the construction industry, the individual who has *control* of a jobsite generally has the responsibility for the means, methods, sequence, procedures, techniques or scheduling of construction. This responsibility and control of the project site carries with it the responsibility for safety of workers and the public on or about the site. Carelessly using the word *supervise* could lead you into the muddle of safety responsibility, a responsibility that rightfully belongs to the contractor.

15

The word *inspect* is also greatly misunderstood — and misused. Generally, a design professional *observes* the construction as part of his or her construction phase services; *inspection* implies a much more detailed examination. (There are times when use of the word *inspect* is appropriate, as in a reference to special government-mandated inspections of certain structural elements of a building, but these are highly specialized services, fraught with risk, and require both a comprehensive workscope and extraordinary contractual protection.)

Optimism is often reflected in the things we say and do. In fact, optimistic words (*better* instead of *worse*, *advance* rather than *retreat*) are used about four times as frequently as their antonyms. In the design professions, however, optimism can be a liability trap. To protect yourself, it is wise to avoid words of promise like *guarantee, warrant, certify, ensure, assure* and *insure*. Unless you can absolutely state or promise something without qualification, you must refuse to assume the role of risk taker. (See Chapter 4, page 89.)

Your choice of words should correctly describe your intent. *Will* or *shall* are words of positive affirmative action — a promise that the act will definitely happen. Use them only when they are actually intended. If you can't be that definite, *may* or *endeavor to* would be wiser choices.

Two techniques may prevent your becoming entangled in lawsuits over word meanings.

First, find more exact words. If you are an average design professional, you use about 2,000 words in your day-to-day conversation. If that seems like a lot, consider this: There are about 600,000 English words. The King James

Bible uses about 8,000; highly intelligent people have vocabularies approaching 15,000 and Shakespeare used 34,000 different words in his works! Make the effort to broaden your vocabulary and discover more precise words for what you want to say.

Second, seek feedback. Since most English words have varying connotations, a good method for testing communication is to have listeners feed your communication back to you in their own words. Engineers, architects and contractors, as members of a team effort, must think and act as a unit. Any ambiguities or misunderstandings that exist within this team can lead to errors, delays, disputes and even litigation.

Using the Right Word in Construction Documents

Do contractors routinely seek clarification and direction after receiving your documents? If so, this may indicate that your plans and specifications contain ambiguous directions.

For example, how often do you use the words *furnish, install* and *provide* interchangeably, intending that they all mean the same? Check their meanings, though, and you will discover considerable differences. In the dictionary you will find that *install* means to "set in position and connect or adjust for use"; *furnish* means to "equip with what is needed"; *provide* means to "furnish, supply...to make available."[2] As you can see, the words are not synonymous. *Install* does not convey the meaning that the item to be installed is to be supplied by the same party installing it. Similarly, the words *furnish* and *provide* do not connote that after an item is supplied, it will also be fixed in place. It is important to be precise.

(17)

Design professionals use many words that have very special and limited meanings to others within their field. The average layperson finds it almost impossible to understand this jargon, especially since there is no one standard definition for most of it. An understanding of meaning is acquired only through long experience and exposure to the working vocabulary of the construction industry.

To further complicate matters, even the same design disciplines located in different geographical areas assign different meanings to the same words. A phrase such as "all standard options as required for satisfactory performance" may have a much different meaning to a contractor in Texas than to one in Maine.

Some words are so susceptible to misinterpretation and so difficult to explain to a contractor (or, worse, to a jury) that you need to substitute another word or phrase to describe a particular activity.

Consider these examples:

Engineering Jargon	Use These Words Instead
Approve	Work is in general conformance
Inspection	Construction observation
Or equal	Or equivalent
Satisfactory operation	Operation as specified

If we take a closer look at two of these words, we can see why they can cause problems for unsuspecting design professionals.

Approve

- The design professional intends the word *approve* to mean to give limited, conditional or qualified permission to use material, equipment or methods, and interprets the word to mean that the submittal or construction referred to should be in general conformance with construction document requirements.

- The dictionary, on the other hand, says that *approve* means "to sanction, consent to, confirm, ratify" or "to be favorable toward, think or declare to be good."
- The layperson (possibly a member of a jury) may interpret *approve* as unqualified acceptance.

The professional liability implications of the word *approve* can be significant. In fact, even using the word *approval* and placing limitations on it might be hazardous. Judges and juries have a tendency to view limited approval with suspicion and have, on occasion, considered it a waiver of the original standards required of the design professional and disregarded the intended limitations.

Or Equal

- The design professional intends the phrase *or equal* to mean that an item should possess the same performance qualities and characteristics as the one specified, and fulfill the function without any decrease in quality, durability or longevity. There is no implication that items must be identical in all respects if the above general requirements are satisfied.
- The dictionary defines *or equal* as "of the same quantity, size, number, value, degree or intensity."
- The layperson may interpret *or equal* to mean the items are identical in all respects without any difference.

You can now see why you should be very careful with the words you use. Instruct your specifications writers and checkers to watch for words that have more than one meaning. If there is any doubt about the meaning, choose a different word or define the word in a glossary or specifications definition section.

Be especially cautious with words you use to outline the scope of a contractor's responsibility. Remember, contractors who understand your specifications can sharpen their bid figures. On the other hand, contractors

19

who are forced to guess your intent may pad their bid to protect themselves against uncertainties, real or imagined. They may assume the worst case and bid accordingly, or they may install the least expensive items inferable from your ambiguities. (Specifications are also discussed in Chapter 4.)

Finally, review the specification yourself before it is issued, remembering that any portion of a specification that has more than one interpretation is incorrectly written.

Red Flag Words

Think twice before you use any of the following words in your contracts. There is almost always a better choice available to you.

administer	control	inspect	shall
advise	direct	insure	sufficient
all	ensure	maximize	suitable
any	equal	minimize	supervise
approve	estimate	none	will
assure	every	optimize	
best	final	oversee	
certify	full	periodic	
complete	guarantee	safe	

Your Correspondence

In addition to the general communication rules already suggested, there are other, more specific procedures you can use in your office to improve your written communication and help prevent misunderstandings.

First, try to have all external correspondence that concerns projects or plans reviewed by a senior member of your firm — a project manager, department manager or principal — before it is sent out. Careful use of the written word takes experience and most principals and managers have developed this skill. Their review of correspondence will provide a cross-check to discover misstatements and avoid misunderstandings.

The result should be:

- *Correspondence of a higher quality*

    If employees are aware that letters will be reviewed, letters will be written more carefully.

- *Absence of ambiguous, imprecise or extreme language*

- *Elimination of errors and typos*

    Letters with errors in basic English, grammar, spelling or punctuation are evidence of sloppiness and can only hurt the design professional's image.

- *Reduced risk of defamation suits by eliminating inflammatory or derogatory statements*

Communicating with Your Client

It can't be said too many times: Never make the mistake of overestimating a client's knowledge of your duties and procedures. Just as the public may not understand the role of a design professional, so a client may not understand the limitations of your profession. It is your job to explain to him or her just what it is you do as a design professional and what it is you do *not* do.

It may seem inconceivable to you that a client could think that you are responsible for a perfect set of plans and specifications, have detailed knowledge of every item you specify or participate in actual performance testing before you write your specifications. Even so, claims are often made against design professionals regarding specifications of products or systems, usually after the standard guarantee periods given by the contractor and equipment manufacturer have expired. A client who does not grasp your professional obligations may allege that you were negligent in specifying an item or that you should have personally tested the system before you specified it. Make sure you provide your clients with the information they need to understand your responsibilities and limitations.

For instance, assume you made the decision, after some deliberation, to omit an item from the drawings or specifications for a project. As construction progresses, circumstances change. It now seems reasonable, in your judgment, to add the item to the project as extra work.

When you made your original decision, it was reasonable and within the legal standard of care, and you probably saved the owner some money. Now, however, the owner, faced with a change order and the resulting increased cost, decides to "misunderstand" your duties. One basis of the owner's complaint will likely be that you were negligent in not specifying the item originally. Another allegation may be that you implied a warranty that the drawings would be complete and sufficient for the purpose intended.

Neither of these allegations may be true. Yet, somewhere along the line you failed to let your client know exactly what to expect from you or your drawings. Your client should have been prepared to expect changes as a normal part of the construction process. Instead, because your professional role was misunderstood, you face litigation.

Another misunderstanding surfaces in suits arising from persons injured at the construction site. Again, it is commonly believed you have an active role in determining the contractor's safety procedures and programs. Your contract and the general conditions of the contractor's contract should be perfectly clear on this issue.

A third area that frequently confuses clients concerns your opinions of probable construction cost. Each time you use the phrase *cost estimate* with a client, you might run the risk of a claim. Why? Because what you intended may be misunderstood. The client may believe that your estimate is a guaranteed maximum figure and will budget accordingly. If the final costs exceed your estimate, the client may argue that he or she properly relied on your expert evaluation. Instead, when you are required to provide information on the expense of an item or project, it is better practice to use the phrase *opinion of probable cost*. This correctly conveys the idea that ultimate costs may — and often do — vary from your opinion and gives you valuable flexibility in defending your efforts. (Opinions of probable cost are also discussed in Chapter 4, page 97.)

The solution to many of these problems is to talk to your client. From the earliest conceptual meetings, through the refinement of your workscope and negotiation of your contract, during the development of your design and into construction, make sure your client is "on board" every step of the way. Explain the problems that can — and will — occur during design and construction. And at all times, be very clear about your role and limitations in the process.

Communicating During the Project

Some design professionals do not take the time to sit down with other parties to a construction project. Often this is simply an oversight. Most architects or engineers are quite willing to answer any reasonable direct question a contractor may have. It would be rare to find a design professional who would not welcome the opportunity to discuss with a client the relative merits of one type of system as compared with another. Yet, unless you initiate regular discussions with these individuals, they may get the impression that you are too busy or too important to be bothered.

To keep the lines of communication open and to enhance feedback, try to meet regularly with other parties to a construction project. On large projects, schedule project review meetings on a weekly basis among representatives of the contractor, the client and the design consultants involved. These sessions can often pinpoint construction problems before they occur or become serious, and permit solutions that are satisfactory to everyone in a non-crisis atmosphere.

Plan internal conferences weekly on a formal or informal basis for each project. Make it mandatory that project professionals recount their progress over the past week, list problems that still need solutions and make requests for whatever information is necessary but has not been received. Reports of this type also serve as a diary of project progress. (See *Exhibit 3*.)

Written progress reports to clients are valuable, too. As part of a client communications program that includes personal visits and progress review meetings, they can help form a bond that will keep you and your client working together even if adversity strikes. Nothing demonstrates a professional approach as effectively as well-planned, timely transmission of clear information.

Documentation

Memory failure or incomplete understanding on the part of the practicing design professional can cost huge sums of money and precious time if litigation results. Design professionals often expect to remember the details of important telephone discussions or conferences concerning an active project without the help of notes or other memory tools.

Exhibit 3 Progress Report

Progress Report

MARTIN & ASSOCIATES, Ltd.
3456 Sylvandale Ranch Hwy.
Scarsdale, CA 93999

Date: 5/12/94   Client: Pachyderm Corp.

Present: R. Bastian   Project: Headquarters Bldg.
         J. Sculley
         J. Martin
         W. Crandall

1. We received the approved schematic design phase drawings dated 5/10/94 and are proceeding immediately on the design development phase as requested by the architect.

2. The problem of the floor space assigned for the mezzanine level (17th floor) was resolved on 5/11/94 and prints of the final arrangement (XA-12 through XA-17) will be marked with our comments and sent back to the architect before 5/18/94.

By: _____
                    John B. Martin
                    Project Manager

Copies to: J. Sculley
           S. Rodale
           W. Crandall
           R. Bastian
           H. Higgins

25

No one remembers everything. It is important to record all your discussions which may in any way concern or influence a project. Memorialize meetings and telephone conversations with clients, subconsultants and contractors. As a matter of routine, require that all discussions involving design decisions be documented by brief memoranda. (See *Exhibit 4.*) A written record helps jog the memory and enhances communication; it may also prove important in the event of the claim. These memoranda and logs are particularly useful if, for some reason, the principal project professional cannot continue and another professional unfamiliar with the project is required to take over and complete the work.

26

Exhibit 4 Conference Memorandum

Conference Memorandum

MARTIN & ASSOCIATES, Ltd.
3456 Sylvandale Ranch Hwy.
Scarsdale, CA 93999

Date: 5/9/94   Client: Pachyderm Corp.

Present: R. Bastian   Project: Headquarters Bldg.
         J. Sculley
         J. Martin
         W. Crandall

Location: Conference Room

Discussed the problem on 17th floor mezzanine. The present floor-to-floor
dimension does not permit the installation of the mezzanine due to restricted
height. Because the 17th floor will also contain an auditorium, the architect
has proposed the floor-to-floor dimensions be doubled on this level. The
proposal was accepted by the client, subject to review of schematic drawings
of the proposed revision.

By: _____
                                              John B. Martin
                                              Project Manager

Copies to: J. Sculley
           W. Crandall
           S. Rodale
           R. Bastian
           H. Higgins

Summary

- Many claims against design professionals result from a breakdown in communication between parties to the construction process.

- To avoid confusion, it is important to avoid using extreme words, words of promise or words with more than one meaning.

- Ambiguous words and jargon can also cause problems, especially in specifications.

- To improve the quality of your firm's written communications, make it a point to have a principal, project manager or department manager review all correspondence before it leaves the office.

- Never make the mistake of believing a client understands your duties and procedures. It is far better to continue communicating with him or her throughout the life of the project.

- To keep the lines of communication open and to handle problems as they arise, make certain you meet regularly with other parties to the project.

- Document all discussions that may concern or influence a project.

[1] *Words and Phrases Permanent Edition,* West Publishing, 1971, 1987-88.
[2] *The American Heritage Dictionary of the English Language,* Third Edition., Houghton Mifflin Company, 1992.

29

AVOIDING AND MANAGING DISPUTES

We might as well say it straight out: you can't avoid conflict. The construction project does not exist that hasn't seen some kind of misunderstanding, disagreement, problem, unforeseen event, design error or construction defect. Not all of these situations evolve into disputes, however, and not all disputes become claims or lawsuits.

There are many reasons why problems can get out of hand. First, the construction industry has grown so large and complex that many participants to a project do not know each other and may not expect to work together again. They may feel they have no stake in developing or maintaining good relationships. Besides, owners may be highly leveraged and/or underfunded. This gives rise to severe scheduling and budgetary pressures that can strain what may already have become adversarial relationships between the parties to the project. Then, too, as we pointed out in the last chapter, parties to a project may simply fail to communicate effectively with each other. Many architects and engineers, for instance, are hesitant to discuss a project's downside with their clients. Then, when a problem inevitably surfaces, the client may feel angry or betrayed and a claim almost always results.

There is still another reason. Everyone involved in construction today is so alarmed by the specter of litigation that they may approach each new project in a defensive crouch. Some design professionals, clients and contractors are advised by their attorneys to begin to build a legal file from day one of the project. Yet, expecting and preparing for litigation may encourage the other parties to act in a similar manner. The situation can be likened to two countries — who know or care little about each other — arming for war. The more warheads one country stockpiles, the more the other must accumulate just to maintain parity. In the meantime, a grim truce is sustained between the parties, who continue to expect the worst from each other. With this attitude, the worst is usually what they get.

So, too, with construction projects. Just as no one can win in an all-out nuclear confrontation, neither is there a winner in a construction lawsuit — except perhaps the lawyers. For the rest of us, the costs are simply too high.

The solutions, then, must lie somewhere other than in a courtroom. Admittedly, it is a big step forward from the brink of war to the peace table, but it can be done. There are some very practical techniques that can help.

Planning for Problems

Many disputes are cumulative. Unresolved small problems create antagonisms between the parties and make it more difficult to resolve new conflicts as they arise. And it is not uncommon for parties who disagree with a design professional's decisions to wait until the end of the project to address all of the unresolved disputes that have arisen. While they are waiting, though, their unstated expectations continue to go unmet, and the level of antagonism rises. In a vicious circle, as relationships deteriorate, the cooperation so vital to the success of a project also erodes. Mistrust may begin to cause delays and disruptions, which in turn cause added costs that then breed still more problems.

Against this volatile background, the stage is set for a serious dispute. When the final straw (perhaps an error — serious but otherwise forgivable) occurs, it may be too late for negotiations.

The longer the resolution of a problem is put off, the more expensive it is to correct. As time goes by, what might have required only a quick and relatively inexpensive solution becomes a difficult and costly defect to remedy. It costs money to remove and reinstall work. It costs a lot more money when you put the dispute in the hands of attorneys. The truth is, no matter who is ultimately found responsible for a defect, everybody loses if the matter is allowed to go to litigation.

How can the parties to a construction project avoid litigation? Perhaps the best and least expensive way is to *have a project-wide commitment that at the first indication of a problem, participants will work together to resolve it and not allow it to escalate into a dispute where third-party resolution is required.*

33

The Role of Relationships

Let's begin by considering one conflict and how it might be handled. Two days before substantial completion, an owner discovers cracking in the support columns of her underground parking structure. She communicates this fact to the architect and the contractor. The architect, in turn, talks to the structural engineer. A meeting is arranged.

The stage for conflict is set if each party fears being forced to shoulder the cost of repairs. Each party has an individual interest. As long as any party advocates a condition or position that is contrary to anyone else's, there will be attempts to *win*, causing others to *lose*.

Imagine, however, that the contractor and the design professionals have worked together on several jobs in the past. What if they like working together? Would this history change the outcome of their meeting?

Common sense (as well as the findings of social scientists) indicates it would. Bonds of loyalty and cooperation built up over time do not dissolve during a crisis. In fact, successful resolution of difficult situations tends to cement these bonds — and creates *trust*.

The guidelines for establishing trust are relatively straightforward. To begin with, trust requires at least one person willing to risk something. During our underground garage meeting, for example, the structural engineer might propose that an expert, agreed upon by all, be hired to study the situation and evaluate the cause of the cracking. This indicates he is willing to put his fate in the hands of an impartial third party.

Trust also demands open and unbiased *communication*. One way to do this is to try to put yourself in the other parties' places. Several things are accomplished by this exercise. First, you may discover another party is, in fact, right. Second, you may discover another party has been making decisions based on incomplete or faulty information. Third, although another party may be wrong, at least you have demonstrated you understand that party's point of view.

Parties who are aware that their relationship will be of brief duration are more likely to resist agreement. Let's assume the contractor in the preceding scenario is working outside his normal geographic area of operations. He has not worked with this project team in the past, and it is unlikely he will work with them in the future. Therefore, the contractor might be considered an "outsider." Regardless of the other factors bearing upon this particular meeting, there is a likelihood that he will be asked to shoulder the consequences. His resentment could very well block a peaceful resolution.

On the other hand, if all parties to the conflict have had and anticipate a long-term relationship, cooperation is more likely, if only because they fear that the tables may be turned in the future or that not cooperating means not working with the others again.

Because of this concern, a number of firms are now entering into long-term *strategic partnerships*. This kind of alliance may take many forms. But in general, *strategic partnerships* refers to agreements between companies to cooperate in order to achieve their separate but complementary objectives.

For example, BSW International, a Tulsa, Oklahoma, practice, has many strategic partnerships and actively seeks clients who will commit to several projects. One such strategic BSW partner/client is Wal-Mart, which has commissioned hundreds of projects. BSW has also established successful long-term alliances with many of its design subconsultants and suppliers.[1]

Strategic partnerships make a great deal of sense. For one thing, these alliances promote better quality and productivity from both parties. The owner and design professional develop an understanding of each other's requirements and procedures so that communication is enhanced. Disputes are more easily resolved. Finally, because it is in the interest of both parties to profit, they tend to have equitable agreements that properly allocate the risk borne by both.

Project Partnering

In looking for ways out of the litigation trap, we often find ourselves turning to the "old timers" of the design professions for some answers. These are the architects and engineers who have stubbornly insisted all along on dealing with other parties to the project in the old fashioned way: by treating each other fairly, with respect, and by *talking* to each other.

The old timers have a point, and today's construction project participants are coming to realize this. Many owners, contractors and design professionals are putting a new spin on an old idea and calling it *project specific partnering* (or simply *partnering*).

Just like the old timers' ethic, the concept behind today's partnering is simple: to dispel the adversarial "us-versus-them" approach often found on today's construction projects and to promote a "let's-all-pull-together" mind-set. The goal is to create a shared vision of the project. While the actual steps may vary, the process usually involves team-building activities to help define common goals, improve communication and cultivate a problem-solving attitude among key representatives of the design and construction team — *before* work on a project begins.

36

Typically, partnering involves a retreat or a series of workshops with representatives from all parties to the project. A third-party facilitator conducts team-building activities that result in a mutually agreed-upon charter or mission statement. The goals usually address such concerns as scheduling issues, jobsite safety, issue resolution procedures and the budget. Key to successful partnering are the follow-up progress checks as well as a final evaluation after project completion.

For partnering to work, it must be owner-driven and have the full backing of the top management of all participating team members. The owner must be committed to the idea, must be willing to incorporate the concept of partnering into the bid solicitations, and must take the necessary steps to ensure that the process begins during (or before!) the design phase.

The benefits of partnering can be significant. The quality of the project is improved. The workplace tends to be safer. The design professionals' roles in the problem-solving process may be enhanced and designer participation in construction phase services is more likely. Partnered projects tend to be brought in on time or even ahead of schedule. What's more, the process typically helps reduce cost overruns. Best of all, there is a reduced exposure to litigation for all parties to the project.

Partnering does not guarantee that disputes will not arise — modern construction is too complex and involves too many parties to eliminate disputes altogether. Rather, it is a way to manage and resolve the disputes that do come up. An essential element of partnering is deciding upon procedures to resolve those disputes.

Partnering has had great success and holds even greater promise for the future. It is a straightforward and proven mechanism to handle construction

37

disputes as they once were handled — before we began to put all our problems in the hands of attorneys.

Jobsite Dispute Resolution

You, the owner and the contractor should decide at the beginning of your project what steps you will take during construction to resolve problems as soon as they arise. There are several techniques to accomplish this. Two of the most effective — step negotiations and dispute review boards — are often implemented together.

Step Negotiations

Step negotiations really amount to a commitment to solve a problem as soon as possible at the lowest possible level of management. If parties directly involved cannot resolve a problem at the jobsite, their supervisors then meet to work out a solution. If they, in turn, cannot agree, then the problem will be passed on to higher management in both organizations, and so on. Often each of these parties is identified at the beginning of the project and there may be a predetermined time limit for resolving an issue at a given level. For instance, if a problem cannot be fixed in two days at the first level, then it is passed to the next decision-making level, which meets and has four days to find a solution. Because passing on a problem to one's boss means having to report a failure, there is incentive to settle disputes very quickly.

Dispute Review Boards

Many parties to construction projects have adopted a "standing neutral" concept. This is an agreement between the owner, contractor and (usually) the design team to mutually select an independent dispute resolver to be at hand throughout construction. Generally consisting of one or more industry experts, this resolver is sometimes known as a *dispute review board (DRB)*.

Dispute review boards (also called *standing mediators* or *standing arbitrators*) have several advantages over conventional dispute resolution processes. DRBs are set up at the beginning of a project and continue throughout the project's lifetime. Because the board frequently visits the jobsite, there is continuity and familiarity with the parties and the specific job at hand. Disputes are often resolved quickly and fairly while the facts are still fresh in everyone's mind. Complaints without merit are discouraged. Everyone involved on the project is encouraged to communicate fairly and to resolve problems on-site and at the lowest possible decision-making level. In fact, parties to projects where DRBs are established have found that the very existence of a board tends to encourage participants to resolve problems themselves — through step negotiations or similar mechanisms — before referring them to the board.

The success of DRBs is impressive. Since the late 1970s, when the first boards came into existence, hundred of projects have instituted DRBs. Of the completed projects, *not one* has had any litigation.[2]

When a Problem Arises

Your goal, therefore, should be to build dispute prevention mechanisms into every one of your projects by instituting partnering and/or dispute review boards and by obligating the owner and the contractor to report problems as soon as they are noticed. With these mechanisms in place, you can work together to mitigate a problem quickly.

Although it is a worthwhile goal, not all design firms will be able to institute partnering, step negotiations and DRBs on every project. If your project doesn't have a formalized dispute prevention and resolution system in place, you need some kind of plan to deal with problems or incidents as they arise.

39

Everyone in your firm should know what to do — and not do — when there's trouble. Many design firms have developed their own "fire drill" or early action procedures and hold a company-wide review from time to time.

What to Do If A Problem Arises:

1. Remain calm.

2. Report the incident immediately.

3. Keep seeking alternatives and solutions.

4. Don't automatically assume you're responsible, no matter what the facts first seem to indicate.

5. Communicate.

6. Document and photograph.

7. Try to resolve the conflict with the others involved. If direct negotiation fails, seek mediation with a third party.

If you are developing your own crisis management procedures or need guidelines for handling problem situations, keep the following suggestions in mind:

Remain calm.

When an accusation is made by a client or contractor, many design professionals feel angry. Your normal response may be to retaliate by countering or striking out at the party making the claim. Don't do it. Examine any accusation calmly and objectively.

Authorities on dispute handling recommend that you assume a neutral attitude, and seek to understand the other party's position. A good response would be:

> *"Please let me have the details. I would like to make notes. I want to be sure I fully understand what you are saying. Let me get this straight. You feel that the plans were lacking in what way?"*

40

This is much better — and more productive — than a quick and heated denial.

Report the situation immediately.

Don't wait until someone has made a formal claim against you. If you recognize an incident or potential claim situation as soon as it occurs and act to resolve it quickly, you may be able to forestall a claim or lawsuit. Be sure your staff understands that reporting such a situation is positive behavior to be rewarded, not punished. All personnel in your firm should know whom to contact — perhaps your project manager or another designated member of management — as soon as they become aware of a problem. That party, in turn, should investigate and notify your insurance claims representative or professional liability insurance agent at once. Often, these individuals can provide guidance and even help diffuse the problem before it escalates.

Unfortunately, sometimes there is a reluctance to report a problem to an insurance company because of the misconception that once a potential claim is reported, costs begin to mount. Actually, the longer a problem is ignored, the more expensive and difficult its resolution is. The time to bring expert loss prevention resources to bear is when they can be most effective — as soon as there is *any* indication of a problem.

Sometimes you may not even know what the problem is, but you are aware of disquieting signs: Suddenly, your client stops speaking to you. Or you learn of a project meeting from which your firm has been excluded. Or you hear that another, independent design professional has been on site. If your sixth sense is telling you something is wrong, listen — and report it.

Keep seeking alternatives and solutions.

Often, parties to a dispute overlook the obvious — the need to remain flexible and continue to seek solutions to a conflict before it escalates into a major lawsuit. This is no time for a "bunker" mentality. Allow yourself and your associates the freedom to keep generating ideas for solving the problem. Discuss these initiatives with your insurer. Together, you may be able to come up with a creative solution that will work for everyone.

Don't automatically assume you're responsible, no matter what the facts first seem to indicate.

As we mentioned earlier, one reaction to an accusation is anger. Another is guilt. When confronted with a failure, admission of "wrong" flows either from a sense of guilt (*Did I do that?*) or a desire to mask it over (*What can I do to make this go away?*).

Sometimes, a design professional assumes the blame — and the liability — by asserting, *"It was my fault. I'll take care of it. I'll make sure it's fixed."* A more thorough examination at a later date may prove this assumption of responsibility totally misplaced, since the fault lies elsewhere or alleged damages did not occur.

It is almost impossible to undo the damage done when you mistakenly assume responsibility and communicate it to the other parties connected with the loss. The acceptance of blame is so prevalent among design professionals, however, that it has been given a name: The Good Guy Syndrome. Believe it or not, it appears in a significant percentage of claims situations.

It is important that you recognize that perfection is impossible — it's *expected* that you will make minor errors. If you acknowledge this from the beginning of the project (and explain it to your client), you will not raise false expectations or set standards you cannot reach. Remember, any loss situation involves many factors; don't try to rush to a verdict before all the facts have been evaluated.

Communicate.

Although you should not automatically assume responsibility, don't stop communicating with others. Keep talking and listening. If you keep up the dialogue, you may learn important facts that can help determine what really happened. Certainly, continued communication will help preserve your relationships with your client and subconsultants and may motivate everyone to resolve the dispute quickly.

Document and photograph.

You need to record the facts. All data and correspondence relating to the dispute should be documented. Write down the duties, responsibilities and performance details of the parties involved while they are fresh in everyone's minds. Keep detailed notes on all communications. Never rely on memory.

When a dispute arises, study the plans and specifications and the contract documents. Note those sections that refer to the problem or that specify the duties of the parties to the dispute. If a product is involved, obtain the manufacturer's or supplier's warranties and specifications available while you were developing the plans and specifications. If shop drawings are involved, examine those that pertain to the claim (and note the application).

Notes and records not only help clarify the issue but will also be needed by any defense attorney who may come to your rescue in the event of a suit. Bear in mind, though, that materials you gather may later be subpoenaed, so it is important to stick to the facts and avoid unnecessary and unfounded personal comments.

"A picture is worth a thousand words" still holds true in potential professional liability claims situations. Photographing or videotaping the disputed subject matter is an excellent way of preserving the record for the future. Audio recordings describing visual observations are valuable for refreshing memories and documenting facts as they existed.

Try to resolve the conflict with the others involved. If direct negotiation fails, seek nonbinding mediation.

Responsibility for failure often belongs to several parties. In these "multi-party" disputes, it is important to communicate with everyone involved. Sit down and talk to the other parties. As soon as possible, try to find a solution you can all live with. If informal negotiations fail, with the consent of your insurer, invite a neutral, experienced mediator to help you reach a settlement. Even if nonbinding mediation is not specified in your contract, any party can suggest it at any time. If these processes fail, or are not attempted, the dispute could escalate into binding arbitration or multiple-party litigation. (See *Mediation,* page 49.)

Working It Out: Negotiation

Once a conflict arises, make every effort to settle it at the jobsite and as quickly as possible. Even if you don't have a conflict resolution system in place, try to work things out before resorting to more formal measures. Although emotions may be running high and you believe you are completely (or mostly) in the right, keep in mind the enormous costs that would result should the conflict escalate into a lawsuit. Remember, too, that about 95 percent of all lawsuits will eventually be resolved through negotiation. But many take months or years of expensive legal maneuvering before the parties arrive at the bargaining table. If you and other parties to the dispute need another reason to sit down and negotiate a solution, consider this: *Almost a third of the dollars paid in settling lawsuits goes to the lawyers.*

It is important to get everyone involved to the negotiating table. Some of the parties to a conflict may not join in a negotiation because they believe that the others will solve the problem. Resolution, however, is much more likely if there is active participation by all parties.

Remain flexible. Negotiation may well mean that you will need to give up something in order to resolve the matter to everyone's benefit. Remember our parking structure scenario at the beginning of this chapter? Suppose the structural engineer had been told by other parties in the project that they felt he had a certain obligation for the damages that had occurred. There was no question in the engineer's mind, however, that the loss was clearly attributable to the contractor. He so advised all other parties to the conflict and made it clear that it was up to them to determine responsibility among themselves. He considered the matter settled. Over the next few weeks, he received copies of further written communications on the matter, which he noted and filed away. Three months later, he was horrified to receive a summons and complaint from the owner, naming him as a defendant.

Could he have done something to avoid the lawsuit? Perhaps. The outcome of any conflict depends on how well all parties understand and coordinate their actions. You can never abdicate your responsibility to attempt to resolve a problem and expect to come out unscathed — even though you think you aren't involved. In conflict situations, a decision to select the most favorable outcome for one person can result in distressing results for others. On the other hand, a decision to select a somewhat less favorable outcome by one party may result in a positive outcome for all.

There are three general choices that affect the final result of any conflict. First, you may decide to maximize your own outcome. Assume in the parking structure meeting that the owner decides upon this course of action. She makes a statement to the effect that one or all of the others at the meeting will have to decide how to absorb the unexpected extra expense, because the cracking wasn't her fault and she has no intention of paying for it.

45

Second, you can decide to place the blame on another. For example, the architect may take a position that supports the owner, thereby pointing the finger at the contractor.

Third, you can make an effort to optimize the results for all parties to the conflict. In our example, the architect in the parking structure meeting states at the outset that the purpose of the meeting is to explore ways to reduce the anticipated extra costs and to make an effort to minimize the conflict. With the consent of his insurance carrier, he may note that sharing responsibility, at least at the beginning, will represent a minor expense compared to the cost and disruption of protracted litigation.

All participants in such a negotiation should have the authority to make decisions. Otherwise, they might stall discussions and "play it safe" or "grandstand" for the home office. Representatives who are instructed to act cooperatively perform better in this type of meeting than those who are told to maximize their own organizations' positions. Suppose the owner's representative has been instructed — or believes it will enhance her reputation with the boss — to see that her company bears as little of the extra cost as possible. Her efforts at cooperation will be unenthusiastic and will stall the negotiating process.

Formal Dispute Resolution

If all efforts to resolve a conflict by negotiation fail, you'll have to resort to more structured methods of dispute resolution. This does not mean, however, that your only option is a lawsuit. On the contrary, because of the huge costs in time and money, litigation should be considered a last resort.

It is far better to rely instead on one or more of the *dispute resolution* techniques available. (While many refer to this as *Alternative Dispute Resolution* or *ADR,* we like to think of it as *DR.* Litigation is the *alternative* — and a poor one at that. On the other hand, we know one fellow who

46

defines ADR as A*ppropriate* Dispute Resolution, and we can't quarrel with
his thinking.) The goal of DR is to give opposing parties the opportunity to
settle disputes quickly, at relatively low cost and with a minimum of
emotional involvement and stress. Most DR methods allow for creative
problem solving and help maintain goodwill between the parties — in short,
they create a win-win situation for all concerned.

You and your client should agree in advance that you will try dispute
resolution methods before turning to litigation. That means that your
contract should address the issue and provide you with the flexibility to use
one or more forms of DR as appropriate to your situation. Keep in mind that
if you use a standard professional association contract form, you will need to
amend the document, since many such agreements specify binding
arbitration as a first step in resolving a claim. (For more information, refer to
*The Contract Guide: DPIC's Risk Management Handbook for Architects and
Engineers, 1993* and *AIA Document B511, 1991, Article 7.*)

There are several DR approaches in use today. These range from
consensual, nonbinding procedures to mandated binding procedures. (See
Exhibit 5.) Your insurer and attorney should be well-versed in the benefits
of each approach and be able to suggest the one most suitable for your
particular situation.

First try to resolve your dispute through one or more of the *non-
adjudicative* DR procedures. These include mediations, minitrials and
advisory arbitrations. In these procedures, *participants work to solve their
own problems* rather than place their collective fates in the hands of
someone else.

Exhibit 5 Construction Dispute Resolution Steps

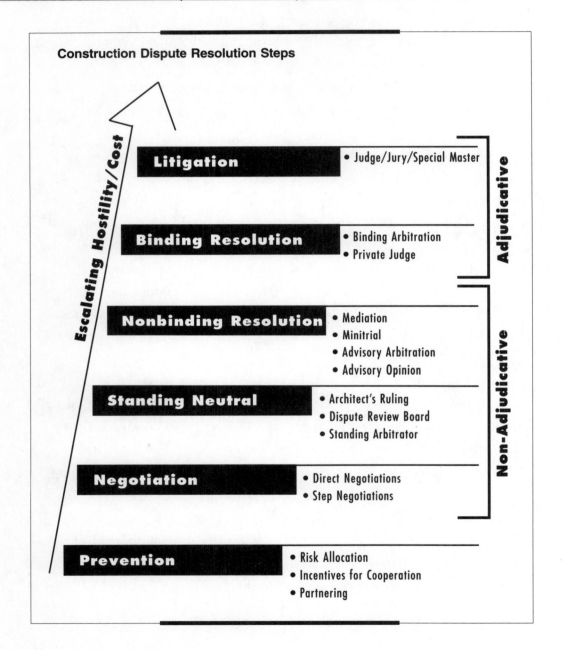

Construction Dispute Resolution Steps

Escalating Hostility/Cost

Litigation
- Judge/Jury/Special Master

Binding Resolution
- Binding Arbitration
- Private Judge

Adjudicative

Nonbinding Resolution
- Mediation
- Minitrial
- Advisory Arbitration
- Advisory Opinion

Standing Neutral
- Architect's Ruling
- Dispute Review Board
- Standing Arbitrator

Negotiation
- Direct Negotiations
- Step Negotiations

Non-Adjudicative

Prevention
- Risk Allocation
- Incentives for Cooperation
- Partnering

Mediation

One of the best DR methods, mediation offers many advantages over litigation or even over the commonly called for arbitration. Relatively quick and inexpensive, mediation can also help the parties settle their disputes while preserving their working relationships.

Mediation is a sophisticated form of negotiation, distinguished by the participation of a neutral third party who helps the parties come up with their own solutions to the problem. The mediator (or *neutral)* acts as a facilitator in the discussions, asking questions and keeping face-to-face negotiations moving. The options available as solutions are limitless — anything decided upon by the parties involved.

Usually a voluntary or nonbinding *consensual* procedure, mediation can be thought of as a three-stage process. In the first stage, negotiations are used to start or improve communication. Ideas and options are explored without requiring commitment. During this stage, the mediator often meets individually with the opposing parties. These discussions are confidential; however, the mediator may be able to use the privileged information — without violating confidences — to advance the dialogue. Many disputes are resolved at this first stage.

If the problem can't be resolved in the first stage, the next stage is designed to clarify facts (sometimes with the help of a neutral expert agreed to by the parties) and to determine costs of settlement.

If necessary, the mediation continues on to a third stage, where the parties may choose another way to settle the dispute: another DR approach, arbitration or litigation.

49

Very often, a mediated result can be obtained in a matter of one or two days — a far cry from the years often required for litigation. Even if mediation is not successful, very often it clarifies the facts in a dispute and narrows the issues that remain to be solved. Mediation is always worth considering.

Be aware that courts in the United States increasingly employ court-ordered, mandatory settlement procedures which they characterize as "mediation." Because they are mandated and the parties are less than open to settlement, this form of involuntary mediation does not enjoy the success of voluntary, nonbinding mediation. Nevertheless, it may help to settle some cases.

DPIC believes wholeheartedly in mediation. We think that every design professional's contract should call for mediation as the first dispute resolution option, before resorting to other DR procedures. Our commitment is such that we offer substantial financial incentives to our policyholders (though our Mediation Works! program) if they resolve their disputes through mediation.

Minitrial

The term *minitrial* may be a bit misleading. More a private nonbinding settlement procedure than a trial, this DR technique allows the legal counsel for the disputants to briefly present his or her case before a panel of top management representatives of each party and, usually, a neutral advisor (often a retired judge or lawyer) in a confidential trial-like setting. Management can then hear both sides of the issues, see the strengths and weaknesses of their respective cases and get a sense of the likely outcome of litigation.

Often this persuades both sides to settle their differences rather than move on to all-out litigation. For this reason, it is important to select management representatives who have full settlement authority and who were not directly responsible for the project.

Unlike litigation, the minitrial is fast and relatively inexpensive — and it is becoming more widely used. One survey of construction industry lawyers showed that nearly 12 percent of DR cases were submitted to a minitrial, and almost two-thirds of those had settled or partially settled.[3] As attorneys become more familiar with the process and its successful track record, more disputes will likely be referred to minitrials.

Other Dispute Resolution Techniques

A number of other methods have been developed to resolve disputes. Some of the more popular are discussed below:

Mediation/Arbitration

Mediation/arbitration is, as you might guess, a combination of mediation and arbitration. The technique, often called *med/arb*, requires one person to act as both mediator and arbitrator. The person, agreed upon by the project parties before construction begins, is selected on the basis of his or her objectivity, honesty and knowledge of the industry.

If a dispute arises, the parties involved attempt to solve it on their own. Failing that, the med/arbitrator is brought in to mediate the dispute. If these efforts fail because the parties can't come up with their own solutions, the med/arbitrator then reverts to the role of arbitrator and issues a binding decision based on his or her findings. Because the parties may be required to use the med/arbitrator throughout the project on additional disputes, the range of conflict usually narrows, and the entire resolution process can be accelerated significantly.

Like any consensual method, for med/arb to be effective, all parties to the project — owners, designers, contractors and subcontractors — must be committed to the process. This commitment can be hard to come by. Some critics of med/arb point out that, whereas mediation is a conciliatory process (during which the parties specify *the least they will take*), arbitration is an

51

adversarial process (during which the parties ask for *the most they can get*). Some also object to the fact that the med/arbitrator learns proprietary information during the mediation process that prevents the parties from maximizing their outcome. Proponents argue that the knowledge gained actually permits the med/arbitrator to construct an equitable solution should arbitration be required. They also note that resolution comes more quickly and the gamesmanship associated with selection of an arbitrator is eliminated.

Mediation-Then-Arbitration

Med-then-arb is very similar to mediation/arbitration, except that the arbitration following mediation is conducted by a different neutral who has also been preselected but does not participate in the mediation discussions. This sidesteps some of the drawbacks of the med/arb method but requires that two individuals be agreed upon.

Voluntary Nonbinding Arbitration

This technique, also known as *advisory arbitration*, is typically used to stimulate agreement before parties resort to a more binding DR procedure. Advisory arbitration is most successful when the resolution of a claim is riding on only a few critical issues. Disputants can make their own rules. They can hear for themselves the decision of a neutral party and discover how their testimony and experts might hold up in court or another forum.

Arbitration

Although arbitration might be slightly less costly, and sometimes (though not always) quicker than litigation in certain situations, it is rarely preferable to mediation. Compared to mediation, arbitration can be time consuming and expensive, and sometimes results in unjust decisions which are not normally subject to appeal. It is important to remember that arbitration, like litigation but unlike mediation, is an *adversarial* form of dispute resolution; a third party makes the decision for the disputants. Parties who arbitrate their differences often emerge with their relationship damaged beyond repair.

An arbitration is less formal than a court trial, although the parties involved are usually represented by attorneys. (This is one reason the costs and time escalate so quickly.) Contracts, documentary evidence and other materials are presented to the arbitrator, witnesses are examined and cross-examined and, since the usual civil rules of evidence are not used, participants are free to argue about the relevance of the evidence. The arbitrator is obligated to consider any evidence that bears on the case, giving appropriate weight to that which is more substantiated and reliable. After both sides have had an equal opportunity to present their evidence, the arbitrator declares the hearing closed. Under American Arbitration Association (AAA) rules, the arbitrator then has thirty days to render the decision, which is binding. The arbitrator is not required to write an opinion explaining the reasons for the decision.

For design professionals, there are some limited situations — small and very simple disputes and disputes in some unique jurisdictions or in other countries — where arbitration may be appropriate. Broad reliance on arbitration, however, is not recommended. Keep in mind that if you sign a contract with a binding arbitration clause, you are agreeing to submit any and all disputes to arbitration. While this may seem like a good idea, it means that you give up flexibility in choosing more appropriate ways to resolve disputes.

There are other potential problems. If you sign a contract in which arbitration is specified as the sole remedy, you may be unable to draw a third party (who is your best defense) into the arbitration proceedings. For example, suppose you specify a type of material or equipment and it fails. If your client calls for arbitration (as you agreed in your contract), you would have no way to make the manufacturer or supplier a part of the proceedings

53

other than as a witness. You would have to recoup your losses by a separate court action against the manufacturer, which will cost you additional money and time, and the matter may not be resolved in your favor.

Another problem with arbitration is that you may not be able to conduct necessary *discovery* proceedings. In a court of law, you can examine your opponent's files; in arbitration, this is usually not possible. It is difficult to prepare properly when you are denied access to evidence your opponent is planning to present to the arbitrator.

In addition, because both parties can present any type of evidence in an arbitration hearing, complicated technical issues sometimes lead to a snowstorm of data that needlessly prolongs and confuses the proceedings.

While most states have laws that make arbitration binding on the parties, some do not. If your state does not, you must go to court to seek an order to enforce the award of the arbitrator — meaning more time and legal expense.

Lastly, under most arbitration rules, if you receive what you believe to be an unfair decision, you cannot appeal it unless you can show fraud on the part of the arbitrator. This can be a real disadvantage if you are clearly in the right, because all too often arbitrators decide disputes by "splitting the baby" in order to settle the case and close their files. For this reason and all the others discussed above, arbitration may not be the best method for resolving your disputes.

Private Litigation

Rent-a-judge, a form of private litigation, refers to procedures in which a retired judge is retained to preside over a faster, more confidential proceeding than regular litigation. Retired justices are not limited to courtroom procedures, however, and may be willing to preside over many other types of DR proceedings as well.

Summary Jury Trials

Often applied in pending litigation, a summary jury trial is usually ordered by the court to get an advisory opinion from a jury as to the probable decision in a case. A summary jury trial gives both parties a "sneak preview" of a jury trial without the expense required for a full-blown court proceeding. Although the jury's decision is not binding, it usually encourages settlement. If the parties proceed with the litigation, the outcome of the summary jury trial is not admissible.

The Breakdown of Communication: When Litigation Becomes Inevitable

If you are able to implement partnering and dispute review boards and/or make use of some of the available dispute resolution procedures, you may be able to avoid litigation altogether. It's a worthy goal. Being involved in a lawsuit is one of the most traumatic and unnerving experiences a design professional in private practice can have. It is financially and emotionally draining and can damage both personal integrity and professional reputation. That is why it is so important to try to resolve crises before they become claims or lawsuits.

Sometimes, however, this just isn't possible. There are those rare times when litigation is the only recourse. For instance, if emergency relief is sought, if you need the power of the court to obtain vital information through discovery from third parties, or if an important legal precedent can be established, then litigation may be the best alternative.

Exhibit 6 illustrates how a case moves through the court system. Although only about 5 percent of all lawsuits filed actually go to trial, those that do typically involve three to five years of complaints and cross complaints, depositions and interrogatories, and interminable motions and counter motions. The final decision is then left in the hands of a jury or judge, people who are probably unfamiliar with, and usually unaware of, the complex practices of modern construction.

The decision to litigate should be made with great care. Your attorney and insurer will consider and discuss the options with you. If no other dispute resolution method seems viable, then litigation may be the answer. Just as in conflicts between nations, when the stakes are very high, important principals are involved and all other avenues for peace are exhausted, sometimes you've got to go to war.

56

Summary

- Every project experiences problems, but not every problem evolves into a dispute and not every dispute grows into a claim. In many cases, project participants can anticipate and avoid potential problems.

- If parties to a conflict anticipate a long-term relationship, the likelihood of cooperation in solving problems is much greater.

- Some design firms are entering into strategic partnerships with clients or subconsultants in order to promote quality, productivity and loyalty from all parties.

- Project partnering can reduce claims and cost and schedule overruns, and can enhance the quality of the project.

Exhibit 6   Litigation and the Court System

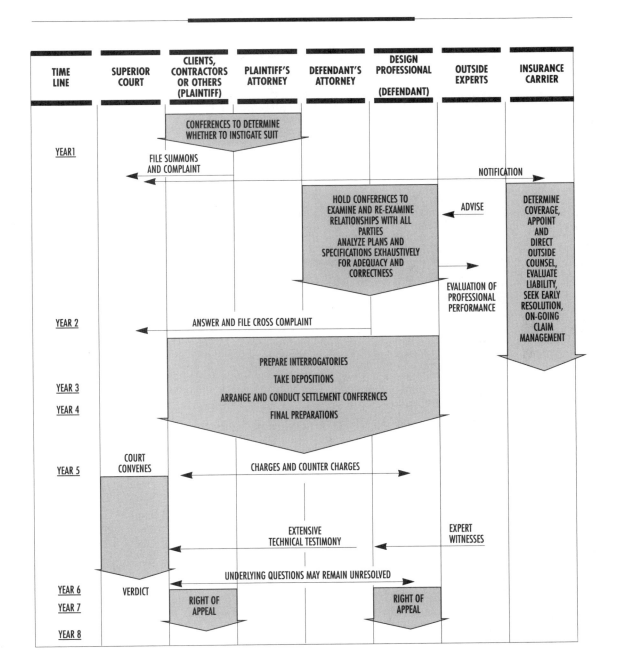

57

- It is important to anticipate and plan for problems before they occur. Have in place a mechanism by which disputes can be reported, addressed and resolved as soon as possible.

- An in-house crisis management procedure will let all personnel in your firm know what they must do or not do in the event of a problem.

- To avoid a claim (and possible litigation), make every effort to settle a dispute at the jobsite and as quickly as possible.

- Dispute review boards have an advantage over other dispute resolution methods in that they are set up at the beginning of a project and continue throughout the project's lifetime. Other DR methods usually start after the project has been complete for some time.

- With negotiation, you may need to give up something in order to resolve the matter to everyone's benefit.

- Litigation should be avoided if at all possible; instead, rely on one or more of the dispute resolution methods available, such as nonbinding mediation.

[1]*Architecture*, October, 1993.
[2]*Avoiding and Resolving Disputes During Construction*, ACEC, 1991.
[3]Thomas J. Stipanowich, Douglas A. Henderson, *Preliminary Report on 1990 Survey of Members of the ABA Forum on the Construction Industry on Nonbinding ADR*. (Prepared for publication in *The Construction Lawyer*, October 1991.) Preventing and Resolving Construction Disputes, Center for Public Resources, Inc., NY, NY.

BUSINESS PRACTICES

There is a direct connection between your approach to professional practices and your exposure to professional liability claims. That is why your loss prevention efforts must extend to your business practices and why the management of your design firm requires just as much attention and expertise as the design of its projects.

Think about your business operations. If you try to incorporate state-of-the-art techniques and materials in your design services, why rely on roll-top desk business practices? When you take a businesslike approach to your practice, you can manage it more effectively and reduce much of your risk.

Project Selection

It isn't always easy to pick and choose your projects. Yet careful selection is essential because accepting the wrong assignment almost guarantees professional liability problems. In making your selections, you need to weigh every aspect of your potential projects.

Several factors have an enormous impact on your risk exposure. Claims are much more likely when you ignore the warning signs in one or more of these areas: *the type of project you choose, the kind of client you work for, the adequacy of the project funding, your scope and fees, your firm's capabilities* and *the fairness of your contract*. Each of these is just as important as the preparation of your plans and specifications.

Consider the example of a mechanical engineer in a small town who was asked to design air conditioning system modifications for an old building to which a new addition was being attached. No reliable record drawings of the original system were available.

The owner vetoed tearing into the walls or ceiling to map the existing system as "too expensive" and asked the engineer to base her recommendations upon a visual inspection only. She did so, but failed to take steps to protect herself with appropriate disclaimers in her contract and in her final report. Later, during construction, when the system's components, ductwork and piping were exposed, they were found to be in poor condition and inadequate for the new addition. To make matters worse, asbestos was discovered in the insulation. To deal with these conditions, the engineer made additional recommendations which required additional and costly modifications.

The owner had used the engineer's original report as the basis for the contractor's workscope. The owner accepted the engineer's modifications as necessary, but because the engineer had not included this information in her original report, the owner made a claim for the additional cost, alleging "errors and omissions."

What went wrong? The design professional seemed to have acted in a perfectly reasonable, ethical and professional manner. If we look at the entire transaction and the decisions within the engineer's control, however, we can see the mistakes that led to this claim.

The engineer did not recognize clear danger signals when considering the *risks of the project.* When she was informed by the owner, for instance, that insufficient funds were available for conducting exploratory demolition to determine the condition and location of the existing system, she should have detected the signs of a poorly financed project.

Furthermore, the engineer should have included in her contract and report a precautionary statement indicating that no design or construction budget involving renovation of existing structures and systems should be based on the preliminary information provided, and that additional expenditures might well be necessary after the existing structure was opened up.

She should have anticipated the possibility that asbestos would be present in an older building. The liability implications here are so great that on *any* remodeling or restoration project, the agreement should contain language noting that if asbestos or other hazardous materials are discovered, the design professional is not responsible for any claims resulting from the existence of the materials, or for the removal or additional costs the removal will necessitate.

63

Clearly, had the engineer been alert to potential problems, she would have spotted the warning signs. Even if she had elected to proceed with the assignment, she could have substantially protected herself by informing the client of the risks and by arming herself with special provisions in her contract.

Assessing the Risks of a Project

Some projects are so litigation-prone that only the most foolhardy architect or engineer would dare accept them. Even if desperate for assignments, few designers would be likely to take on the classic designer's nightmare: a conversion to condominiums of a thirty-year-old cliff-hanger apartment house adjacent to a hazardous waste dump site on an earthquake fault line — recently purchased by a group of financially over-leveraged neurosurgeons and their lawyers.

While the above cliché may be overly obvious, there are other high-risk projects that should be almost as easy to spot. These may involve troubled sites, hazardous waste, asbestos, underfinanced clients, amusement parks, prisons, highly controversial projects, litigious clients and, yes, condominiums.

Sometimes claims-prone opportunities are not so easily identified. These could include fast-track projects, which can involve substantial modifications to plans and, thus, big change order expenses — and irate owners. In this situation, very unsophisticated clients can be a big problem. They rarely comprehend your role as a design professional or the construction process. They won't expect or understand changes and, most likely, will not understand the need to have sufficient contingency reserves set aside in their project budgets. Assignments that would omit your construction phase services or, conversely, require construction observation on someone else's design should also give you pause.

Then there is the "contractually hazardous" project. This could be *any* type of project — even a simple, plain vanilla assignment — for which the client issues a contract containing such unfair or onerous provisions that you could wind up accepting most or all of the client's liability. Typically, the client issues a purchase order or similar contract form, which is thoroughly inappropriate for engaging a design professional's services. Some might argue that such a project is the riskiest of all because you have none of the standard contractual provisions a professional needs for protection.

Project selection is rarely a cut-and-dried, yes-or-no affair. For most design professionals, potential projects usually contain two or more secondary risk factors that, considered separately, might be acceptable, but together could add up to a big liability headache. Take, for example, a well-financed but naive client who wants to build an apartment complex as a speculative project. You might be able to educate an unsophisticated client, you tell yourself, and perhaps negotiate a solid contract. But can you protect yourself from the subsequent purchaser of the complex? What could you do if the apartment complex goes condo in a few years and the complex suddenly has 300 new owners?

Your best course is to learn to identify all the potential risks on a prospective project. Some architects and engineers use a Project Evaluator like that shown in *Exhibit 7* to evaluate both their clients and their projects before submitting a proposal or negotiating an agreement. This can save a lot of time and money spent chasing projects you really shouldn't accept.

Next, determine how the risks you've identified might be managed. You can transfer some risk to another party, such as an insurer, or to your client through contractual provisions known as *indemnities*. You can minimize some risk by educating your clients, by providing more comprehensive services and by insisting on qualifications based selection (see page 77) and

65

Exhibit 7   Evaluation of Risk–Red Flag Checklist

Evaluation of Risk   Red Flag Checklist

Prepared By: _____   Date: _____

Project: _____

Location: _____

Client: _____

Type of Contract: _____   Owner: _____

Estimated Fee: $ _____

PROJECT TEAM MEMBERS

	Owner		Architect		C/M	
	Yes	No or Don't Know	Yes	No or Don't Know	Yes	No or Don't Know
1. Does this project team have sufficient experience for this type of project?						
2. Is this party financially stable and/or do they have clear credit rating?						
3. Does this party have a relatively claims free history?						
4. Does this party have a good reputation in the community?						

PROJECT CONSIDERATIONS

	Yes	No or Don't Know
5. Does our firm have a proven track record with clout?		
6. Is the fee determined by negotiations rather than bidding?		
7. Are there adequate human resources?		
8. Is there adequate scope of services?		
9. Is construction review included?		
10. Is the project free of unfamiliar code requirements?		
11. Is the project located in a geographic area where we have experience?		
12. Is the schedule realistic?		
13. Will the project design be completed before construction begins?		

FUNDING

	Yes	No or Don't Know
14. Is this project adequately funded?		
15. Are funds for unexpected contingencies included?		
16. Can this project be realistically designed within budget?		

Exhibit 7   Evaluation of Risk—Red Flag Checklist (continued)

KNOWLEDGE OF PRIME CONTRACT WITH OWNER

	Yes	No or Don't Know
17. Is a mediation clause included?		
18. Is a Limitation of Liability clause included?		
19. Are any clauses with special insurance requirements reasonable?		
20. Is there a requirement for subs' insurance?		
21. Are the end-user requirements clearly stated?		

HIGH RISK PROJECTS

Check the types of project that apply.

22. a. Condominiums
     b. Production housing
     c. Developer Project Commercial building over nine stories
     d. Commercial building, over nine stories
     e. Renovation project
     f. For inspection only
     g. Municipal building
     h. New technology is needed

RISK IDENTIFICATION RESULTS

SECTION	Number of Checks Under "No or Don't Know"
PROJECT TEAM MEMBERS (1-4)	
PROJECT CONSIDERATIONS (5-13)	
FUNDING (14-16)	
KNOWLEDGE OF PRIME CONTRACT (17-21)	
	Number of Checks
HIGH RISK PROJECTS (22)	
TOTAL	

Considering your score, if you have a check in any category, carefully consider if you should:
> **1. Take the project as offered.**
> **2. Take the project only after negotiating any mitigating factors.**
> **3. Turn down the project.**

Use the section below to provide an explanation of the ways any identified risks will be mitigated.

COMMENTS

Signed (Evaluator)

negotiation with a competent contractor. You can significantly reduce your risk by developing a contract that is fair and precise, that accurately defines the intent of both parties (see page 81) — and that includes a *limitation of liability* clause (see page 95).

You and your client have to take a good, hard look at the risks you cannot prevent or control. Understand that on a high risk project, the risk must be borne by the party best able to control it. If no one can control a risk, then it must remain with the project owner. If the owner refuses, you should decline the project.

The risks that remain on your plate — those that cannot be otherwise transferred or managed — will require a hard-headed business decision. Is the fee or fame incentive so attractive that you can afford to take the chance? Making that determination may be the biggest gamble you take.

Evaluating Your Client

As you can see from the preceding discussion, it is extremely important to know who your client is and what kind of business he or she runs before agreeing to accept an assignment.

You should know the answers to these questions:

- Does the client have a realistic budget and schedule?
- Is sufficient funding available? What is the source of the funding?
- Is your client going to be the owner and user, or is the project being developed for speculative resale? Are the end-user's requirements known?
- Will the contractor be selected on qualifications or on price alone?
- Is the client sophisticated and does he or she understand the construction business?

- Does the client have the ability to manage the project?

- Will you be working with people who have the authority to make the decisions you need?

- What is the client's experience with this type of project?

- Does the client have a history of claims and litigation?

- What is the client's reputation for integrity and honesty?

- How did the client get your name? Why were you selected by the client?

- Is the client willing to adopt mediation or other dispute resolution techniques?

- Is the client willing to institute partnering on the project?

- Is communication with the client clear and direct?

- Is the client's personality compatible with yours?

- Has the client shopped around for a low fee? Does the fee allow you to provide services that are sufficient to protect your professional integrity and do a reputable job?

- Does the client have a reputation for slow payment (or nonpayment) of fees?

- Is a good contractual relationship possible with the client, or is the client rigid and uncompromising?

- Are the client's program and quality expectations achievable? Are they achievable within the agreed-upon budget estimates?

69

Your relationship with your client has a great deal of influence on the likelihood of a lawsuit. It may be impossible to have a good relationship if you have fundamental disagreements with your client about the way business should be conducted. Determining this before the project begins may save you a lot of trouble. If you sense your client does not measure up on the important issues, run, don't walk, to the next project.

A Matter of Money

Many of the questions in the preceding list focus on financial considerations, and with good reason. Obviously, you should avoid any project that seems to be insufficiently funded or whose budget and expectations are not in line with one another. In other words, if your client expects to build the Taj Mahal but has only enough rupees for a bungalow, you're headed for trouble.

An astonishing number of claims against design professionals can be traced, at least in part, to the fact that the owner or the contractor did not allocate enough money or have sufficient funds available to do the necessary work. You would think that this problem should concern only the owner, the contractor and their respective financial institutions — and not you, the design professional. Not so. When the inevitable unanticipated costs and extras arise and the dollar squeeze begins, you will find yourself vulnerable to a desperate owner or contractor who, midway through construction of the project, is looking for scapegoats and money from any available source — including your pocket or your insurer's.

For example, consider the owner and contractor who have committed all their resources to a large project. Midway through construction, the owner discovers that the cash flow demands are mounting far beyond his capacity. The slightest delay or unanticipated expense magnifies the problem. His reaction is, unfortunately, quite predictable. In a desperate attempt to keep his head above water and fend off impending foreclosure, he adopts a typical tactic. Payments to the contractor and you, the design professional, are slowed or stopped, and the blame is placed on you. The contractor has a better bargaining position than you do, because the owner needs the contractor to finish the job. You, however, have rendered most of your services, and are just waiting to get paid — including payment for your additional services with funds the owner had been "sure" he would have by the time construction began, if you would just help him get his permits.

The slightest ambiguity in the contract documents is made to order for a claim against a design professional. The all-too-common reaction of an over-stretched owner is to refuse to pay you, claiming faulty performance of your duties. The scenario goes something like this: As you press for payment, the finger pointing begins. You claim breach of contract and sue for collection. The owner countersues (you can count on it). The owner may even have initiated a preemptory claim against you to discourage your collection efforts. In either case, he or she will say that the cost of extras and the resulting delays are due solely to your negligence in not providing sufficiently clear drawings and specifications, in delays and errors in shop drawing review, and in whatever other reasons a fertile imagination can invent.

The fact that the owner's claim is eventually found to be without merit is of little consolation when you consider the not-so-hidden costs of having to defend yourself. These hard dollar costs — such as your insurance deductible, your time and that of your staff in defending against the claim, and loss of revenue due to bad publicity — as well as the months and years of resulting stress, can take a terrible toll on you and your firm.

Therefore, routinely check the financial capability of each client for every project before you agree to commit your services. After all, you are about to invest your payroll dollars up front in the expectation that you will be fully paid for these services. You should not have to wait weeks or months to discover the client cannot pay you. On a project with a public owner, make sure that the project has been authorized *and* that enough money has been appropriated or otherwise set aside to complete the project. A public agency

71

employee signing an agreement with you is not proof that the project has been authorized or that funds are available.

You should also explain to every client that unexpected needs will arise during the project and that the client must maintain an adequate contingency fund throughout the course of construction to meet these needs. You are entitled to see some assurances that the client has budgeted for this contingency or otherwise has the necessary funds available, such as a commitment from lenders.

Checking a Prospective Client's Financial Condition

There are five basic tools you can use to evaluate a potential client's financial condition. All of these steps should be done after securing your client's permission in writing:

- Review of the client's financial statements
- Review of the client's credit history
- Information from the client's bank
- Review of public (land) records
- Discussions with other design professionals who have worked for the client

A review of the financial statements will indicate the client's liquidity, assets and debts. Don't be shy about asking for such statements. Clients often ask you for this information; you are entitled to the same privilege. You should ask to see current statements as well as financials from previous years. Your firm's chief financial officer or your outside accountant can assist in analyzing these statements.

Credit rating agencies or credit bureaus gather and disseminate information about the credit worthiness of individuals and businesses. Reputable credit

72

agencies belong to the Association of Credit Bureaus. You may subscribe to the services of these credit organizations and order their reports.

Credit reports typically give, among other data, the following information on all credit transactions:

- Date of last payment
- Highest credit given
- Current balance owed
- Times past due by category (30-45 days past due, for instance, or 45-60 days past due)

A bank will generally confirm that an individual or company has an account; however, it will not indicate the specific balance. It may indicate whether the balance is high, medium or low, and when the account was opened.

Public records contain transactions involving real estate. They also contain attachments on real estate, such as liens, lis pendens, mortgages and judgments. Does your client have a history of projects that were liened by contractors or other design professionals? If so, consider that client risky. Does the project have a list of mortgages in excess of the value of the land or, worse still, in excess of the completed project? If so, you probably won't want that client.

Perhaps the best way to get a sense of how a potential client views financial obligations is by talking to other design professionals who have worked with him or her. Ask your client for the names of design firms he or she has used in the past. Then contact these design professionals to ask if payment was prompt. If there were problems, try to learn what happened. This will help you decide whether it is worth investing your valuable time in the client.

73

If you decide to proceed with the client, you are entitled to adequate contractual terms regarding billing and payment of your fees, no matter how credit-worthy he or she appears to be. You need the leverage of the contractual right to suspend your services and to withhold your plans unless you are paid. Your contract must contain clear provisions regarding your remedies if you are not paid on time. Interest, the right to attorneys' fees, lien rights (if available), termination — all of these measures can put teeth into your contract and help you collect your fees.

Your Professional Fees

You are entitled to a fair fee for your professional services. When a prospective client attempts to induce you to work for a fee you consider inadequate, you should be prepared to refuse the project. Before you do, though, investigate whether the prospect's attitude concerning your fee comes from insufficient information. Educate your client by letting him or her know that a reduction in professional fees may actually result in a higher cost of construction or operations or in the assumption of great risk by the client.

One design professional uses this letter to explain:

> Thank you for giving us the opportunity to provide design services for you. From your description of your project, we are sure we would enjoy working on it. The magnitude and degree of complexity of your project, however, would require more design effort than we could afford to schedule at the fee you suggest.

> We are sure your budget has been carefully calculated and we know you have a responsibility to keep the cost of the project within certain limits. Our experience shows, however, that sometimes one point is overlooked: the life cycle cost of a project will in part be determined by the skill and competence of the professionals who design it. In fact, the total cost of a project (including the design fee) may often be reduced by more thorough planning, investigation of materials and construction observation. If you have inadvertently omitted this consideration from your

budget study, we are sure you will not resent our calling it to your attention. It could save you money in the long run.

If you agree, perhaps we can discuss the project further. We plan to call you in a few days, and if you have any questions we will be happy to answer them. We look forward to further discussions with you and your staff.

If you approach the discussion of your fees in a straightforward and professional manner, you can often obtain the work you want without sacrificing your interests or increasing your exposure to liability. Some clients can be naive. They may truly appreciate such a professional inquiry.

Even if a client is not uninformed, just by addressing these issues you show that you understand the risks (both the client's and yours) of the project and that you care about the project's success.

Many successful design firms steadfastly refuse to negotiate fees. Instead, when faced with a client who wants them to lower fees, they turn to their scope of services and ask the client to choose which service he or she wants to omit. Without increasing their risk, the design firms are sometimes able to reduce or delete a particular service or portion of the project. If the client tries to reduce the scope of services (and related fees) to a level that is insufficient to do the job properly, however, these firms have the professional discipline to decline the project.

Here, again, careful project selection comes into play. Learn to consciously analyze the risks on a prospective project and to balance them against the reward you stand to gain. If the risks are substantial, the rewards had better be, too. Recognize that the risk of a dispute is not the only risk you face. There is also the risk of increased insurance premiums because you are taking on a high-risk project or because a claim will have resulted from that project. In an extreme situation, you may even be risking your future insurability!

Bidding

Sometimes a prospective client who is unfamiliar with your firm asks you to give a quote for design services but expresses no interest whatever in your qualifications. If this strikes you as worrisome, you are thinking *loss prevention*. That type of inquiry is a clue that the prospective client may be a "shopper," is underfinanced, inexperienced or simply not very smart — someone who should not be high on your list of desirable clients.

The design professional encounters two types of bid situations. In the first, fee is the sole criterion used by the client in selecting a design professional. It may become obvious when you receive a set of specifications and a request for a written bid or when the client says he or she intends to hold a price-only negotiation.

The connection between bidding or price-only competition for design services and professional liability claims is clear. Projects awarded to design firms on the basis of the lowest bid are usually underscoped and are often subject to costly claims. The scope of design services for such projects may be pared down to below the normal standards of professional care, with inadequate or nonexistent construction phase services, for instance.

In a typical price-only scenario, a prospective client wishes to retain your firm to perform design services. During discussions, the client carefully emphasizes such considerations as the prestige of the project, the public relations value of having one's name associated with such a project and the likelihood of additional, more profitable work in the future if all goes well. The prospective client then tells you that you are not the first firm with whom they've worked, and that there has been dissatisfaction with past services performed by one of your competitors. You are told the client would be willing to consider retaining you, provided your fee is "reasonable" (*Translation: cheap*). They point out the relative simplicity of the design proposed for the particular project, implying that nominal effort would be needed to perform the services.

The client then goes on to say, "One of your competitors who did our work previously charged us x percent of the actual construction costs for their work even though the projects were not complicated. If you will agree to design the building for half that price, we have six more buildings coming up in other cities which will need to be designed." (*Translation: You'll lose a little on each job, but you'll make it up in volume!*)

When faced with this type of bid situation, try to change your potential client's way of thinking by pointing out the misplaced emphasis on low-cost design. (Refer to the letter on page 74.) Explain that if the client is willing to pay for better quality through more comprehensive services, you may be able to reduce the life cycle costs of the project, thereby saving him or her a great deal of money in the long run.

In the second type of bid situation, the client tells you that your fee is being evaluated, along with other criteria such as expertise, references and qualifications. In this situation, you need to decide the minimum amount for which the project can be competently completed, using your best estimating and prior project cost experience, while allowing for contingencies that may increase that cost both in professional services and construction. You must then sell that figure, *as part of a complete package of design experience and skill,* to the client.

Qualifications Based Selection

The method of procurement for design services that makes the most sense is *qualifications based selection* (QBS). This is the traditional method by which a client identifies and selects the design professional who is best qualified for a project. The client and architect or engineer then discuss the project and develop a workscope. The design professional's fee is determined by that workscope. This method recognizes the fact that designing is a highly subjective and creative process, and encourages design excellence and innovation. It also enhances communication between the design professional and the client. QBS is in everyone's best interest, designer and owner alike. Alternative selection methods usually mean a unilaterally developed scope of services — either by the client or the design professional. If a workscope is not developed jointly, there is a tremendous risk that each party will proceed under differing assumptions and expectations. A client and design professional working at cross purposes or with differing expectations is a claim just waiting to happen.

Instead, help your clients understand that QBS will, in the long run, save money and lower everyone's risk — especially theirs. (For the same reasons, you should practice what you preach and use the same criteria for selecting *your* subconsultants.) Point out that the federal government recognizes that quality means cost-effective design procurement. Two giants of public construction, the U.S. Army Corps of Engineers and the General Services Administration, were instrumental in pushing the Brooks Bill through Congress in 1972, mandating QBS in design service procurement by all federal agencies. Since then, most states have enacted similar legislation that requires QBS in state agency contracts with design professionals.

You may be tempted to work for a fee lower than you feel is appropriate, reduce the scope of your services or participate in a bidding situation. If so, stop for a moment and weigh the expected benefits and "promises" of future rewards against your liability exposure — your risk. The future of your practice could well rest on this decision.

Your Firm's Capabilities

Some design firms submit proposals for specialized projects even though no principal or employee within the firm has the necessary knowledge or experience for such a project. This often leads to a frantic search for qualified personnel if the firm is awarded the project, or the temptation to try to muddle through somehow, turn out the foremost design possible under the circumstances and hope for the best. Consider, for example, the architectural firm trying to move into larger assignments that finally succeeds in landing its first high-rise building project. The firm immediately begins the design, assuming it has enough knowledge to deal with the special demands of a high-rise structure. The professional liability risks created by a firm working beyond its capabilities or comfort zone can be immense.

Perhaps it is improbable the above scenario would happen in your office. The example, however, shows a weakness of some professionals: the inability or unwillingness to recognize their own limits and their firm's true capabilities.

Take the time to review your firm's capabilities. Are there sufficient personnel with appropriate expertise for your normal workload? Are back-up personnel available if a highly skilled person or someone with unique experience were to leave your firm? Evaluate the quality and number of substitutes available should a key player in your operation become unavailable. Before accepting new projects, inventory your personnel records and review their academic and professional experience. Never commit yourself to an obligation you are unable to fulfill. Remember, too, that even if you have the personnel, they may be fully committed to other projects. Which of those projects will you deprive to staff the new assignment? Can you justify these decisions to your existing clients?

A related area of concern is the misrepresentation of professional capabilities. Some design professional firms overstate their qualifications in advertisements, directories, brochures and proposals. These firms often use extreme words and phrases, such as *best, most qualified* or *expert* to describe their practice. At the very least, injudicious wording can set the stage for unrealistic client expectations.

Other firms inadvertently misstate their firm's capabilities. Your firm's qualifications, for example, may be listed in a brochure that is out of date, and apply to personnel who are no longer with the firm. However innocent, this might be considered misrepresentation. Some states have statutes under which this kind of fraudulent misrepresentation can be — and is — prosecuted in criminal court.

Prudent firms keep their statements of qualifications up-to-date. Brochure formats that permit the removal of obsolete data and the insertion of current data will give you the cost-effective flexibility you need to avoid misleading prospects.

Ask yourself, "If there were a lawsuit involving claims of professional negligence, have I made any statement in a brochure, proposal or presentation that would overstate or mislead anyone about our present capabilities?"

If you are sued, your performance will be judged by the professional standard of care; that is, did you measure up to the level of skill, care and judgment normally exercised by other professionals in the community practicing the same discipline under similar circumstances? If you have any doubt about your current ability to perform the services you are proposing in a competent and professional manner, you would be far better off refusing the assignment.

Your Professional Services Agreement

Oral agreements are a thing of the past — or they should be. It is rare today to find a construction project free from controversy. In the event of a dispute, you must be able to establish your rights and obligations. This will be much easier if your part of the bargain is set out in carefully defined terms that do not rely upon the faded or biased memories of the parties involved. Although this point may seem obvious, amazingly, some design professionals still provide services on the basis of a handshake. In no other part of the construction industry do the participants to an agreement deal on such an informal basis. Contractors and suppliers consider a well-drafted contract document an absolute necessity, not merely a convenience.

The need to establish your rights in the event of a dispute is not the only reason to put your agreements in writing. Negotiating a written contract gives you and your client a chance for careful consideration of such issues as the allocation of risk, the duties of each party and a detailed scope of services. In the negotiation process, your client may discover that his or her understanding of the extent of the agreement is quite different from yours. This provides the opportunity for further discussion and clarification — until you can both agree on the terms and conditions. Without a written agreement, defining your workscope, for instance, may be left in the hands of a court and you may discover that the court thinks you agreed to do much more than you ever intended!

A one-sided contract, however, can be as bad or worse than no contract at all. A contract that is written by a client's over-zealous attorney may be so onerous that it places you under an unreasonable burden of performance and obligates you to assume most or all of your client's risk on the project.

81

The subject of professional services agreements could fill a book. In fact, it does: *The Contract Guide: DPIC's Risk Management Handbook for Architects and Engineers* is a good place to begin learning about contracts. The *Guide* discusses contract formation and negotiation in depth, as well as drafting or modifying specific contract clauses into a sound and reasonable agreement. There are, however, some basic points you should master right away. (See *Exhibit 8.*)

Agreements for professional services come in all shapes and sizes. Many architects and engineers prefer to use the standard contract forms (such as the AIA or EJCDC documents) developed by their professional organizations. These forms are excellent starting points, but as these organizations point out, the documents will need to be adapted to your situation. You should review the circumstances of each potential project and then strengthen and/or supplement the standard forms as necessary. Be careful, though. The standard contract forms have been carefully developed and are coordinated with other documents (the General Conditions and subcontracts, for instance). If you plan to amend the standard forms in any way, be sure to use the services of a knowledgeable attorney.

Many firms have developed their own standard contracts. This is an excellent idea. It is far better to have your own well-worded, reasonably protective agreement on tap for a potential client than to wait for the client to offer his or her favorite form. Generally speaking, the party who gets its contract on the table first — or whose draft contract is the basis for negotiation — is the party who will get more of its desired language in the final document. Again, in developing or customizing an agreement, review the language with an attorney and make any necessary amendments to fit your particular project.

Exhibit 8 Your Contract

Your Contract

When negotiating agreements for professional services, keep these points in mind:

- Your agreement should be written clearly and should carefully spell out the duties and obligations of both you and your client.

- Your agreement should be consistent throughout in its use of terms. Ambiguous terms should be defined. The agreement should be complete and integrated with all supporting exhibits and addenda.

- Your agreement should contain a well-defined, mutually developed workscope that spells out both the services you will and you will not provide.

- Your fee should be adequate to cover the services contemplated in the workscope, including those of your consultants.

- The schedule should be adequate to perform all of the contemplated services in a competent and professional manner.

- Your agreement should be purged of overreaching and unfair provisions that increase your liability and jeopardize your insurance. If you cannot delete unfair provisions, at least modify them so they are acceptable.

- Your agreement should specify how and when you will get paid and what happens if you are not.

- Your liability should be limited to an amount that is fair and acceptable to both you and your client.

- Your agreement should state that you and your client will disfavor litigation and use mediation and/or other dispute resolution techniques if you cannot resolve disputes on your own.

- Both you and your client should have the right to terminate the agreement if necessary.

Clients will often ask that you use their agreements. These may run the gamut from relatively benign preprinted professional service agreements to more onerous standard purchase order forms or even a modified general construction contract. In reviewing these documents, you must be particularly wary of attempts to transfer the client's risk to you. Talk to your attorney and try to modify as much of the more onerous provisions as possible. Remember, your client may not really intend that you take on all of his or her risk and may be willing to modify the language so that it is more equitable. On the other hand, if he or she does intend that you shoulder all or most of the liability, is this really a client you want?

When reviewing a contract drafted by a client, you may discover that your own duties and obligations are quite extensive and set out in great detail, but those of the client are quite limited or ambiguous. Be concerned, but don't panic. Most contracts are, in fact, somewhat one-sided when first drafted and will require modifications in order to be acceptable to both parties. It is natural and expected that both parties will make changes, perhaps several times, before the agreement is finalized. Therefore, it is important to take the time to review a proposed contract with care.

Your attorney's advice is extremely important. An experienced attorney who is knowledgeable about construction law, especially in architect/engineer agreements, is a valuable advisor. With your assistance, he or she can suggest modifications that may protect your interests and will be acceptable to your client. This preventive legal review has paid for itself time and time again. The more familiar your attorney is with your practice and your prospective contractual commitments, the more effective he or she can be in steering you through the dangerous waters of liability.

Don't overlook the contract review assistance your professional liability insurance agent or broker can offer. Often, they are well-versed in contract review and are willing to help you spot and modify those provisions that could expand your liability or be difficult to insure.

Your Scope of Services

One of the best ways to avoid misunderstandings about a project is to make sure both you and your client have a clear picture of the other's expectations and assumptions. A client who agrees up-front on which services you will and won't provide is a client who is less likely to be confused about your responsibilities should a problem develop later.

Work with your client to develop a well-defined scope of services that clearly sets forth those services you *will* perform as part of your basic services, those services you *can* perform as an additional service, those services you *will not* provide and those services your client understands must be provided but *by someone else.* This last point is very important. You can be liable for failing to perform a service — even though you were not hired to do it — if you should have informed your client of the need to have the service provided by someone else. Talk to your client about services he or she has decided to exclude and come to a definitive agreement on who will provide them. Besides being good loss prevention, this discussion often gives you the opportunity to outline other services you offer of which your client may be unaware.

You should keep in mind that it is risky to take any type of assignment that reduces the scope of services below that which is normal and usual for your profession. For example, agreeing to perform design without the construction phase services may be unwise. To do so denies you the opportunity to clarify minor errors or ambiguities in your plans and specifications or to answer questions that will, inevitably, arise in the field during construction. What's more, a court may decide that, although you did

85

not contract to provide construction observation services, a reasonably prudent design professional would have.

To help you think about all the possible services for a particular type of project, it is a good idea to use a scope of services checklist or matrix. You can use the basic services listed in the standard AIA or EJCDC agreements as a starting place, or you may want to develop your own. (See *Exhibit 9.*) Your chart should be specific to the services that are normal and customary in your discipline and for the type of projects you perform. Such a checklist can be used as a planning device to ensure that all possible services are considered, which could then be a guide in estimating or pricing your proposed services. The same checklist or a derivative thereof could then become a part of your proposal to your client. (Bear in mind that if the checklist becomes a part of your proposal, it may likewise become part of your contract by reference or incorporation.)

It is also an excellent idea to list those services that are not included, such as soils engineering (geotechnical), surveying, or hazardous waste removal. You should also list detailed tasks, such as providing record drawings or detailed cost estimates, that you will not perform.

Deal Breaker Clauses

Beset by runaway construction costs, poor results and frequent claims, owners, too, have sought to defend themselves. Unfortunately, they have sometimes overcompensated by adding onerous clauses to their contracts, often in the form of one-sided indemnities, warranties or liquidated damages provisions. While at one time these defensive provisions were limited to contracts between the owner and the contractor, increasingly they are finding their way into contracts between the owner and the design professional.

Exhibit 9 Scope of Services Checklist

Scope of Services

BASIC SERVICES	Included	Not Included	Remarks
Project Development Phase			
1. Define Scope of Structural Services			
2. Assist in Development of Schedule			
3. Assist in Determining Channels of Communication			
4. Assist in Determining Responsibility for Dimensions			
5. Assist in Determining Drawing Standards and Specifications Format			
6. Assist in Determining Number of Meetings and Number of Site Visits			
7. Negotiate Fees and Payment Schedule			
8. Execute Contract			
9.			
Schematic Design Phase			
1. Attend Meetings			Max. of
2. Establish Structural Design Criteria			
3. Prepare Studies of Alternative Structural Systems			Max. of
4. Assist in Selection of Structural System			
5. Provide Structural Criteria for Geotechnical Consultant			
6. Assist in Determining Need for Special Studies			
7.			
Design Development Phase			
1. Attend Meetings			Max. of
2. Prepare Preliminary Foundation Drawings			
3. Prepare Preliminary Structural Design Calculations for Typical Elements			
4. Prepare Preliminary Framing Layout Drawings			
5. Prepare Typical Detail Sheets			
6. Identify Pre-Engineered Structural Elements			
7. Prepare or Edit Outline Specifications for Structural Items			
8. Assist Preparing Preliminary Opinion of Cost of Construction			
9. Review Results of Special Studies			
10. Coordinate Structural Design with Special Design Criteria			
11. Submit Design Development Documentation for Approval			
12.			
13.			

Exhibit 9   Scope of Services Checklist (continued)

BASIC SERVICES	Included	Not Included	Remarks
Contract Documents Phase			
1. Prepare Structural Design of Primary Structural System			
2. Designate Elements to be Designed by Specialty Engineers, and Specify Structural Criteria for Specialty Engineers Design of Pre-Engineered Structural Elements			
3. Review Effect of Secondary or Non-Structural Elements Attached to Primary Structural System			
4. Attend Meetings			Max. of
5. Assist in Coordination with Building Code Officials			
6. Complete Structural Calculations			
7. Complete Structural Drawings			
8. Prepare or Edit Specifications for the Primary Structural System			
9. Assist in Establishing Testing and Inspection Requirements			
10. Perform Checking and Coordination of the Structural Documents			
11.			
12.			
Construction Administration Phase			
1. Bidding and Award			
a. Assist Evaluating Bidder's Qualifications			
b. Provide Structural Addenda and Clarifications			
c. Assist in Bid Evaluation			
2. Pre-Construction Services			
a. Attend Meetings			Max. of
b. Assist in Establishing Communications Procedures			
c. Assist in Establishing Procedures for Testing and Inspections			
d. Assist in Confirming Submittal Agency			
e. Assist in Selection of Testing Procedures			
f. Advise Client and Contractor Which Structural Elements Require Construction Observation by SER			
g. Respond to Building Department and Peer Reviewer Comments			
3. Submittal Review			
a. Review Specified Submittals for Items Designed by SER			
b. Review Submittals for Pre-Engineered Structural Elements			
4. Site Visits			
a. Make Site Visits at Intervals Appropriate to the Stage of Construction			Max. of
b. Prepare Site Visit Reports			
5. Materials Testing and Inspections			
a. Review Testing and Inspection Reports			
b. Initiate Appropriate Action to Those Reports, if Required			
6.			

Adapted from CASE Document 2-1993, Coalition of American Structural Engineers

What should you do if your client stands firm on a contract that contains one or more of these undesirable provisions? First, find out if your client truly intends to have you assume unreasonable liability. If he or she does, then you must stand firm, too. Explain that what is being asked of you is beyond the scope of your responsibility and is not insurable. Frequently your insurance coverage is not broad enough to protect you against the liability you are being asked to assume in an unreasonable contract clause and, therefore, you or your firm are at risk if you agree to the client's provisions. This should be of concern to you *and* your client. If your client persists in being unreasonable and refuses to delete or change language that would place you in an untenable position, then *you must walk away from the project.*

Bear in mind that a clause can be made unacceptable by the addition of a single word. In Chapter Two, we explain how some words used in an agreement can obligate you to far more liability than you intended to accept. (See Red Flag Words, page 20.) Words such as *any, all* and *every,* or *inspect* and *supervise* can be as hazardous as the most one-sided indemnity.

The following examples illustrate a few of the more onerous (what we call Deal Breaker) clauses you may encounter in client-proffered contracts. The list is by no means comprehensive. We suggest you also refer to *The Contract Guide: DPIC's Risk Management Handbook for Architects and Engineers* for more information.

Indemnities

Look carefully at any contract your client asks you to sign. Often, this document contains the words *save harmless, hold harmless* or *indemnify* somewhere in the provisions. Make no mistake: if a client is asking you for an indemnity, the client is probably asking you to assume some of his or her liability — to shift his or her risk to you. In fact, it is likely that you are being asked to take on more liability than required by law or custom. Such a provision may not be covered by your professional liability insurance.

Here's an extreme example — what our claims department calls the "Indemnity from Hell":

> *The Design Professional agrees to defend, indemnify and save harmless the Client, its officers, directors, shareholders, employees, agents, attorneys and any of their assigns from any and all liability, claims, demands, suits, actions, proceedings, loss, costs and damage of every kind and description, including attorneys' fees, interest, court costs and expense, which may be brought or made against the Client because of injury or damage to persons (including claims for the death of any person or persons) or property, received or sustained or arising from or in any way connected with, in whole or in part by reason of any acts or omissions of the Design Professional, the Client, contractor, subcontractor or subcontractors, or any of their employees.*

If you agree to such a clause, you would assume liability for the entire project! Of course, most indemnity provisions are not so obviously unfair, but many do ask for unreasonable concessions. In particular, watch out for indemnities that would have you:

- Indemnify the client for the client's own negligence or that of the contractor or subcontractor
- Indemnify the client totally for claims caused only in part by you
- Indemnify the client against allegations, demands, suits or claims of your negligence
- Defend the client (i.e., to provide an attorney for the client's defense)
- Indemnify other inappropriate parties, such as a client's agents, contractors or attorneys

In fact, beware of any provision that asks you to indemnify the client for anything other than your proven *negligent* acts, errors or omissions.

When confronted with an indemnity, your best course is to eliminate the provision altogether and explain that the law obligates you to perform in a non-negligent manner anyway. If your client insists on some sort of indemnity, try to persuade him or her to agree to a mutual indemnity in which each of you indemnifies the other for your own negligent acts. If that is not possible, you may have to unilaterally agree to indemnify your client — but do so only for that portion of the damages that arises from your negligence.

Most insurance underwriters are extremely cautious about the type of indemnity agreements they will insure. They do not ask you to shirk your legal responsibility, but they are reluctant to insure any assumption of liability that properly belongs with someone else. Before you agree to any indemnity, review the language with your attorney and your professional liability agent or broker.

Liquidated Damages

A provision for liquidated damages is a perfect example of a Deal Breaker clause that has no place in a professional services agreement, yet often appears in owner-drafted documents. While not uncommon in owner-general contractor agreements, this provision is inappropriate in design professional contracts. Liquidated damages are a specified amount agreed upon in advance to represent damages to the owner, usually because of delay, when it may be difficult to compute the actual damages. For instance, if each day's delay is agreed to represent a loss of $500 to the owner, then a delay of 10 days means that the owner is due $5,000 in liquidated damages.

91

Because you cannot control the many unknowns of performing a unique design service for a particular project, you cannot assume responsibility for delays that may occur, unless you are negligent. If you are proved negligent, you are liable for only the actual, provable damages caused by your negligence. Get rid of any liquidated damages provision and, if your client objects, explain that the clause is not insurable under your professional liability insurance and is inappropriate for your type of contract.

Certifications, Guarantees and Warranties

Some owners try to include *certifications*, *guarantees* and *warranties* in their contracts. All three of these terms are a type of promise — you are promising your client that a certain result has been reached, a standard has been met or a statement or condition is true, correct or perfect. These provisions were originally intended to address dissatisfaction with construction or manufacturing workmanship, but they are now creeping into professional service contracts. A warranty may be fine for a television set, but not for your services.

Here is one example of a dangerous warranty clause:

> *The Design Professional warrants that all services rendered under this agreement shall be performed by persons who are extraordinarily skilled and in accordance with the highest standards of their profession. The Design Professional further warrants that all construction work performed on this project will conform to the plans and specifications and will be fit and sufficient for the intended purpose.*

A clause like this can create serious professional liability insurance problems. You are hired because of your professional knowledge and skills, and the skill level at which you should perform is governed by the ordinary standard of care of your profession. Under that standard, you are not expected to be perfect and you do not have to guarantee your work or the work of others. If you certify or warrant your services, you are promising perfection and you assume a level of responsibility far beyond the normal standard of care — and that is not insurable. If, as in the above clause, you also guarantee someone else's work, you are assuming that person's liability as well — another uninsurable action.

You may have encountered a clause like this one:

> *At the completion of the project, the Design Professional will certify that all of the work has been performed in strict accordance with the Design Professional's plans and specifications.*

If you agree to the above clause, you are really promising your client that you will make certain that the contractor has completed every bit of his or her work according to your design. Unless you have someone standing next to each worker every single day observing every aspect of the work, you cannot possibly know such a thing, let alone guarantee it to your client.

Neither of the foregoing provisions belongs in your contract. Delete any clause that requires you to certify, guarantee or warrant anything you cannot know for certain and explain to your client that such language is uninsurable.

Convincing Your Client

What if an otherwise good client wants you to provide a warranty, certify your work or indemnify him or her? Each situation will, of course, have to be treated individually. Personalities play an important part. Nonetheless, a good client should be willing to listen, and will usually accede to your wishes if you explain in logical terms why you cannot extend your liability.

93

This delicate subject was successfully handled with a letter from one firm:

> We notice that this purchase order form has been specifically designed for the purchase of materials and equipment, and that some of the terminology is not normally contained in an Architect/ Engineer agreement. We make particular reference to Paragraph 6, which suggests a warranty that the services provided by us will be free of design defects. We are, of course, prepared to state that our design and specifications will be prepared in accordance with generally accepted professional architectural practices. A statement that they would be free of design defects is unrealistic.
>
> We have similar reservations about Paragraph 9, which deals with indemnification. We believe it may be appropriate to provide an indemnification clause for the areas in which we are immediately concerned, relative to negligent acts, errors or omissions on our part. However, in the broadest sense in which Paragraph 9 could be interpreted, it would be, for example, an indemnification against elements such as breach of contract or certain intentional torts. We do not believe it is your intent to include such considerations.

Another design professional in the same situation obtained the desired effect by the following letter, which proposed a trade-off:

> We note that your contract of hire contains a hold harmless and indemnity clause. We feel this should be omitted, for several reasons.
>
> We are going to be providing you with our services; this requires that our people be on your construction site, where we have no control over safety.
>
> We will be subjected to operations in connection with the contractors you have hired, who are answerable only to you as to the safety of the jobsite.
>
> Further, we will be exposed to lawsuits by the contractor's workers if they are injured, in their mistaken belief that we have some voice in jobsite safety.
>
> For these reasons, it seems more proper for you to hold us harmless and indemnify us while we are performing services on your behalf. We recognize that such an idea might not be in keeping with your "standard form of agreement" so we will not insist upon this, but we must request that you, at least, delete the hold harmless and indemnity clause from the contract.

This letter made a lot of sense to the client, with whom, incidentally, the design professional had excellent rapport. The better you have educated your client, the easier this kind of agreement is to achieve.

On the other hand, if your client is not willing to negotiate and modify these troublesome clauses, you need to consider if you really want or need to work with this type of client.

A Limitation of Liability Clause

You have been reading about ways to control risk throughout this book. Limitation of liability offers one of the most effective ways for you to control your professional liability risk, by allocating that risk properly between you and your client.

Who should be responsible for how much risk on a project? This is always a difficult question. Historically, risk has not been assigned equitably in the construction environment. Architects and engineers bear far more of the risk than their participation in a project warrants. When an engineer who agrees to perform a "walk through" is named in a large lawsuit, that engineer is bearing a disproportionate share of the risk. Clearly, there must be a better, fairer solution.

There is. Limitation of liability is a contractual way of allocating risk in proportion to the design professional's participation in the project. The design firm says, in effect, "We will provide you with our services at a stated fee, providing you agree we will not be liable for an unlimited amount of money." In other words, the design firm and the client can work together to set some reasonable limit based on the amount of risk the designer is willing to retain. Often that limit is set at an amount equal to the design professional's fee or some other negotiated amount.

The issue is not avoidance of responsibility. Design professionals are just that — professionals who take pride in the quality of their designs. They expect to accept a reasonable level of responsibility for whatever project they undertake. Limitation of liability allows for the acceptance of responsibility but limits that responsibility to a dollar amount agreed to by the design professional and the client.

Some owners have resisted the idea of limitation of liability in the past, but many design professionals are now routinely getting clients to accept such clauses. How do they do it? They are educating their clients about risk allocation. They are explaining that design professionals are often brought into costly suits even if they are not at fault. They are demonstrating to their clients that it is unreasonable for clients to ask design professionals to assume unlimited risk. Most of all, they are simply asking for limitation of liability clauses in every single contract they sign.

There are many variations of a limitation of liability clause, and states vary on how they enforce them. Here is one example:

> *In recognition of the relative risks and benefits of the project to both the Client and the Design Professional, the risks have been allocated such that the Client agrees, to the fullest extent permitted by law, to limit the liability of the Design Professional and his or her subconsultants to the Client and to all construction contractors and subcontractors on the project for any and all claims, losses, costs, damages of any nature whatsoever or claims expenses from any cause or causes, so that the total aggregate liability of the Design Professional and his or her subconsultants to all those named shall not exceed $_____, or the Design Professional's total fee for services rendered on this project, whichever is greater. Such claims and causes include, but are not limited to, negligence, professional errors or omissions, strict liability, breach of contract or warranty.*

You and your attorney should work together to come up with a limitation of liability provision that is suitable for your project and jurisdiction. Whatever variation you use, you will want to make clear in the clause that you and your client reached agreement on it, and that the dollar amount was negotiated. You should also highlight the provision in some way (for instance, with bold type, italics, or a place for your initials and those of your client).

Even though you may not get limitation of liability in every one of your contracts, you should still try. In time, if you put forth the effort to educate your clients, you will succeed with many of them.

Opinions of Probable Cost

When you present a design for a project to a client, invariably the first thing he or she asks is, "How much is it going to cost?" The moment you give a figure, you create the potential for a claim. Most clients do not know the difference between a contractor's bid and a design professional's cost estimate. Many fail to appreciate that your opinion of the costs is not a guarantee of a final project cost. They may not understand that the many factors affecting construction costs are beyond your control, making it impossible for you to do anything other than render a professional opinion. This misunderstanding often gives rise to disputes. If you give your client an estimate that is off by more than a few percentage points, and your client mistakenly thinks your estimate was carved in stone, he or she may claim that critical decisions on financing, timing or feasibility were based on your figures.

Still, clients must have some idea about costs in order to set their budgets. What can you do to fulfill this need and yet comply responsibly? The best advice is to suggest that if your client wants a highly accurate, reliable estimate, he or she should hire a professional cost estimator. If you explain the liability issues involved, your client should understand. If he or she demurs, you could, of course, hire an estimator yourself (although you would still have risk because the estimator would be a subconsultant for whom you are responsible). The cost of hiring an estimator is an issue you and your client would have to work out.

If you must provide the cost estimate, your figures should be conservative and as thorough as possible. Apply the same care and skill to the preparation of your cost figures that you devote to preparing your designs and specifications.

Design professionals are often unduly optimistic when they give cost estimates. In fact, the number of cases of cost estimate problems has been so high and the impact on professional liability claims so significant that some insurers exclude such claims. Although DPIC does provide coverage for claims arising from cost estimates based on your designs, many other insurers do not. If you provide estimates, make certain you are insured for this type of claim.

How realistic are your opinions of probable cost? You can use the chart in *Exhibit 10* to rate yourself. Keep in mind that, depending on your jurisdiction, a judge or jury may feel that if the actual construction cost comes within 5 or 10 percent of your figures, you have made a reasonable estimate.

One way to improve the quality of your estimates is to have someone in your firm other than the person preparing the design develop the estimates. Some firms have a second person merely check the designer's computations. This is not as reliable, because the checker typically does not share the designer's sense of responsibility since it isn't his or her own work. Other

Exhibit 10 Cost Estimate Evaluation

Cost Estimate Evaluation

**Ace & Associates
Architects**
5100 N. Wacker Drive
Chicago, IL 60656

Accuracy score:

Number of projects estimated: **27**

Rating Time period covered:
JAN. 1, 1995 to JULY 1, 1995

Number of estimates exceeded: **4**

% rating: **14.8**

Job Number	Name	Final Cost Estimate	Bid Figure*	Percentage of Estimate		Remarks
95-06	THE ANNEX	833,640	808,480	−	.03	INCLUDES BASE BID PLUS ALTERNATES
95-09	BARNES ARCADE	54,900	62,800*	+	15.0	* BID = 79,200 DESIGN MODIFIED
95-11	CRAFT MARINA	328,580	314,410	−	.04	INCLUDES INCREMENT NO. 1A ONLY
95-41	DOLE CENTER	135,840	125,560	−	7.5	COST PER SQUARE FOOT USED AT CLIENT REQUEST
95-26	ELGIN TOWER	3,795,280	4,313,520	+	13.4	* NOT INCLUDING OWNER FURNISHED EQUIPMENT
95-37	FOXWORTH ACRES	1,574,280	1,384,820	−	12.1	INCLUDES ALTERNATES ACCEPTED
95-46	GAINS CLINIC	203,540	195,780	−	4.0	BASE BID ONLY

*For actual cost or construction price

firms hold meetings to discuss cost estimates. The person who computes the figures must explain the reasoning behind the numbers to senior members of the firm. This puts added pressure for accuracy on the estimator and adds importance to the function. It also requires the firm's manager to be directly involved in the estimating process.

What about the one-person shop? If it is impossible to hold conferences or have different individuals compute the cost estimates, the best course is the second-look approach. We have all heard the adage, "Better sleep on it." A second look after a day or two, even by the same person, is a valuable professional liability loss prevention technique.

Regardless of your past success in predicting costs, the next time you are asked to make a cost estimate, carefully review its purpose with your client. Take extraordinary care to explain what these figures represent — a very general and approximate opinion of cost, which the client can consider, along with other information, to arrive at a preliminary budget for the project. Tell your client what the cost estimate is *not* intended to be. It is *not* a guaranteed maximum figure. The terminology you use is also important — not only in your contracts, but also in your correspondence, memos and the forms you use to give your figures. To avoid misunderstandings, you may want to use the term *opinion of probable construction cost*, which more accurately describes the intent of those figures. Don't forget to include a contingency factor in your opinion of probable cost to deal with the unexpected requirements that inevitably arise. Think twice about working with an owner who refuses to include a contingency fund — he or she may cause big trouble when the extras or overruns occur.

Promising Delivery of Your Plans and Specifications

After asking about cost, the second question a client typically asks is, "When will your plans be ready?" Each time you agree by contract to deliver the design portion of the contract documents on a specific date, you run the risk of being held responsible for costly delays that may result from changes or unavoidable difficulties. Clients frequently make claims against design professionals alleging breach of contract for failure to complete plans and specifications in the agreed upon time. Indeed, agreeing to a specific schedule may be one of your most perilous professional acts.

It is almost impossible to tell at the outset of a project just how long you will need to complete your services. Clients don't tell their dentist how long she should take to fill a tooth, nor do they tell their accountant how long he has to complete an audit. The work of a professional does not lend itself to precise time schedules or firm completion dates. Unanticipated situations invariably come up, many of which are beyond your control. If possible, it is best not to agree in your contract to a specific schedule. If a completion date is required, however, be certain any timeline is reasonable and has an adequate safety margin built in. Furthermore, do not accept responsibility for delivery on a specific date without providing for excusable delays and provisions for extensions of the deadline. Your contract should include a clause excusing you from damages caused by delays in performance that arise out of events beyond your reasonable control.

Remember, however, that even with this provision, you still face the possibility of delay claims caused by factors that *are* within your control.

Many design professionals tend to underestimate time requirements. You may be tempted to shorten your schedule to try to accommodate your client's needs, hoping every possible break will come your way. Even if it

101

means risking the loss of the project, you are better off refusing to commit to a too tight schedule than to wind up in a lawsuit because you failed to make timely delivery.

Working feverishly "around the clock" to meet a deadline can reduce the efficiency of your most competent employees to the point where errors creep into the drawings and specifications. Consider, for example, the design professional faced with a deadline that is virtually impossible to meet. Reacting to extreme pressure from the client, he issues incomplete drawings and specifications with the notation that changes will follow. He then makes a desperate attempt to complete the design and communicate new information to the contractors before the bids are due, but the addenda are not transmitted in time for the contractors to assemble accurate bid figures. In order to cover the cost of contemplated additional work that might be required when the ambiguous documents are clarified, the bidders quote substantially higher figures than they would otherwise have done. In an even more likely development, the contractor issues expensive change orders to correct the omissions and ambiguities that occurred because the design professional did not allow time to carefully check the drawings and specifications. In either case, the owner discovers that the budget is exceeded. The result is a claim against the design professional for delays or cost overruns, or both.

As with cost estimates, having someone other than the project's designer develop projections of the time needed for project delivery can control the tendency to over-promise. (In larger firms, the schedule is generally prepared by the project manager or a principal with input from the designer.) Although the designer understandably feels in the best position to know the nuances and ramifications of the design and the time necessary to produce it, he or she should understand that when an uninvolved design professional prepares the schedule, he or she can often generate an independent — and realistic — opinion.

Use *Exhibit 11* to judge your success in predicting design schedules. It is, of course, easier to follow a realistic schedule than an overly optimistic one. Exceeding a schedule from time to time is normal. But failing to complete 80 percent of your projects on time should alert you to the fact that you are being consistently unrealistic. Before you agree to a schedule that is too tight, study the risks involved. By accepting only those projects where there is sufficient time to do a good professional job, you reduce your exposure to professional liability claims. Here, again, your clients must be educated so they will understand that good plans and well-written specifications do not happen in a day.

Remember, too, that when you agree to a tight or unreasonable schedule, you are committing your subconsultants to the same schedule — and that can be treacherous. Quality work takes time, and there must be allowances for unforeseen events arising during a project that can hold up progress and wreak havoc with the best of schedules.

103

Collecting Your Fees

A look at the accounts receivable files in many offices reveals that design professionals often have difficulty obtaining prompt payment for their services. The problem is so common, in fact, that the average architectural or engineering firm carries its receivables for two months or more. Add in another fifteen to thirty days' lag time between payroll and billing, and a firm's cash flow is easily stretched to the limit. Collecting your fees is a process that, obviously, requires a delicate balance of resolve and tact. If you press too hard for payment, you may lose a client; if you are not diligent, the client may continue to delay payment.

Exhibit 11 Schedule Accuracy Evaluation

Schedule Accuracy Evaluation

Ace & Associates
Architects
5100 N. Wacker Drive
Chicago, IL 60656

Accuracy score:

Number of projects completed: *24*

Number of deadlines exceeded: *3*

Time period covered:
JAN 1, 1995 to *JULY 1, 1995*

% rating: *12.5*

Job Number	Name	Final Deadline	Design Completion Date	Days Late (Early)	Remarks
95-47	JOHNSON BUILDING	JAN 31	JAN 30	(1)	DEADLINE EXTENDED
95-22	MIDTOWN SQUARE	FEB 14	FEB 14	—	
95-04	100 MAIN STREET	FEB 20	FEB 28	8	JOB CAPTAIN ILL FROM 1/6 TO 1/17

A substantial number of professional liability claims results from design professionals' attempts to collect their fees. When pressing a client for payment, many architects and engineers get their answer in the form of a threat or lawsuit alleging errors or omissions in design services.

A typical scenario begins with an architect who performs professional services in accordance with her agreement. At the close of the project, the client takes occupancy and seems satisfied with the result. After sending several invoices for her fees, however, the architect begins to hear of some dissatisfaction from the client. As the architect becomes more and more insistent on being paid, the client becomes more dissatisfied. When the client becomes aware of the architect's intention to sue for payment, he then claims that the architect was professionally incompetent. The architect initiates a suit to collect her $10,000 fee — and the client brings a countersuit alleging professional negligence and demanding damages amounting to $500,000.

The practicing design professional, with a reputation at stake, is particularly vulnerable to a client who chooses this all-too-common business tactic. It is a frustrating situation, but there are measures you can take to forestall the problem. It means, however, that you must be tenacious and thorough in handling the billing and payment side of your business.

As always, your best route is prevention. Earlier in this chapter, we discussed how important it is to choose clients who have a history of paying their bills on time. If you check the credit and payment histories of prospective clients, you can spare yourself a lot of problems later on. That's just the first step, though. You still need to make certain your contracts are very clear on the details of how and when you will be paid and what your rights are in the event of nonpayment. What's more, if your agreement has a provision stating that the prevailing party in a lawsuit is entitled to recoup his or her legal expenses from the loser — called an Attorneys' Fees provision — a client may think twice about threatening litigation as a way of delaying payment. Your contract should also contain provisions that allow you to suspend or terminate your services in the event of nonpayment. Finally, if you have any questions about a prospective client's financial well-being, consider requiring a retainer up-front to be applied to the final billing.

Mail your monthly invoices promptly. (Some firms bill even more frequently.) In addition, you should police the aging of your accounts receivable. A long-delayed payment is a red flag — don't ignore it. It is important to follow up quickly to determine why payments are not being made and to resolve the problem before the project is complete, preferably before you release your plans. If payments are still not forthcoming, invoke your Suspension of Services or Termination contract provisions.

As soon as a project has been completed — when the client's sense of satisfaction and accomplishment is highest — send a final bill and follow up to obtain payment as quickly as possible. You might want to offer a prompt payment discount. Some firms, for example, offer a 2 percent discount for payment within ten days.

Subconsultants

Even though multiple prime projects (in which project owners contract directly with other consultants) are more prevalent now, it is still common to see the more traditional method of contracting (in which the prime design professional subcontracts with numerous subconsultants). Today, it is not unusual for a single large project to involve as many as ten or even twenty subconsultants. Whether your project requires the services of two or twenty subconsultants, these relationships require special attention.

Select your subconsultants as carefully as you (we hope) select your clients. Choose your subconsultants on the basis of their qualifications — just as you expect your clients to use qualifications based selection (QBS) to choose you.

Meet with your subconsultants to get a sense of your similarities and differences. Are your standards of integrity and honesty the same? Are your working styles compatible? Is your design judgment similar? Find out about the subconsultant's staff. Has the project been delegated to senior designers — or to inexperienced personnel?

It makes sense to include subconsultants in early project discussions. If the sub understands the client's expectations as well as the budgetary and scheduling parameters, he or she can provide vital assistance and a unique perspective during the proposal and design phases.

Do we really need to tell you that all projects should have a written subcontract? A surprising number of subconsultants still provide services on the basis of a handshake — at least until they're involved in their first claim. Thereafter, these consultants, poorer but wiser, put their attorney's number on speed dial for contract advice on every project.

Whether you are the prime design professional or a subconsultant, you should select with extreme care the firms with whom you will be working.

When you are the prime design professional, consider the following:

- Does the subconsultant have a proven track record with this type of project? Are adequate personnel and facilities available?
- Is the subconsultant familiar with the latest technology pertaining to this project?

- Does the subconsultant have adequate insurance? Have you received all required Certificates of Insurance?

- Have you checked the subconsultant's references and talked to people who have worked with the sub in the past?

- Have you carefully reviewed your contract with the subconsultant? Will the subconsultant indemnify you for his or her own negligence? Ownership of the sub's instruments of service (plans and specifications) should be negotiated and addressed in your agreement. The subconsultant's workscope should be consistent with your agreement with your client.

- Will the subconsultant subcontract any services? If so, you may want to approve those subcontractors and make certain the sub indemnifies you for those services.

When you are a subconsultant, consider these points:

- Is the prime professional qualified for this project? Check to see if the prime has performed similar services in the area of the proposed project.

- Who is the prime's client? Is there adequate funding? What are the client's financial qualifications?

- How early in the project are you being brought in? Will you have the opportunity to develop your workscope and budget before they are set?

- What is the fee payment schedule? Will the payment of your fees depend on payment by the client to the prime? If so, how soon after the prime is paid will you be paid? If not, how soon will you be paid?

- Is the design schedule realistic? Is there adequate time in which to do your work? Does it allow for a thorough coordination check?

- Will you have access to the client to obtain needed information?

- Is the prime design professional's proposed contract with the client fair and reasonable? Does it call for dispute resolution? Does it contain a limitation of liability clause and are you included? If there is an indemnity from the client, is it passed down to you? Are any other obligations imposed on you?

- How will shop drawings and submittals be handled?

- Will you be allowed to provide construction observation on your portion of the project? If not, who will do so and what are their qualifications?
- Who will retain ownership of your plans or specifications? How are your designs protected?
- Will this be a "partnered" project? Is a dispute review board in place?
- Does the prime carry professional liability insurance? How much? What are the limits? Have the owner and prime looked into project insurance?

A good way to take a lot of the uncertainty out of subconsulting is to foster long-term relationships with firms with whom you prefer to work. (We touch on strategic alliances and partnering in Chapter Three.) You both learn how the other works; you can readily communicate with each other. You understand the other's expectations and can depend on the quality of each other's services. You can establish ongoing master contracts which reflect your mutual understanding of the general terms and conditions, and will require only a service order and workscope for each new project. When both the prime and subconsultant know that each can rely on the integrity and professionalism of the other, they have even more reason to work out any problems that arise.

Project Evaluation

The most effective means of improving the quality of your services is to conduct an ongoing evaluation of performance. It is important to have in place a formalized procedure to review and evaluate each of your projects upon completion. Project review meetings can assess client satisfaction, the adequacy of the time schedule and budget, and the performance of project management, consultants and the project team. Be sure to assess the client, too, to determine if you want to pursue further projects with him or her. You should review in detail what problems were encountered during the course of the project, how effectively they were resolved and how similar problems can be avoided in the future. Many firms have standard project evaluation forms for this purpose. (*Exhibit 12* shows such a form.)

Of course, the ultimate judges of your performance will be your clients. Asking for their evaluation is the best way to determine if you have lived up to their expectations. Upon completion of each project, arrange for a meeting between a principal of your firm and the client. (You may or may not want to include the project manager in this discussion; sometimes the client will be more candid if the PM is not present.) Some firms ask the client for a verbal assessment; others believe it is more worthwhile to have the client fill out an evaluation checklist. In any case, you will want to know if the client feels you understood the project requirements and if you communicated effectively with him or her. You will want to know if you met the client's expectations on time schedule and budget. You will want a frank assessment of the quality of your work, your strengths and your weaknesses. It is important that you listen carefully to the evaluation, answering questions without becoming defensive and noting any problems that need correction — with a promise to respond appropriately.

Personnel Management

A firm's greatest assets are its employees. Above all else, human resources will determine the success or failure of an enterprise. The kind of people you have working for you, their skills, attitudes and training, and your personnel policies can have a tremendous impact on your firm's risk management profile. How surprising, then, that all too often so little planning goes into selecting, training and retaining the people upon which a firm's reputation and future depend.

Finding the right people is the product of a strong personnel policy. Such a policy doesn't have to be complex to be effective. In fact, it should be

Exhibit 12 Completed Project Evaluation Form

Completed Project Evaluation Form

Ace & Associates
Architects
5100 N. Wacker Drive
Chicago, IL 60656

Instructions

1. The attached COMPLETED PROJECT EVALUATION FORM should be filled out by the principal and project architect in a joint meeting. Other key staff may assist if required.

2. The following questions should be answered in writing. If additional space is required use separate sheets and attach.

3. If problems or discrepancies in our professional services are discovered, they should be discussed in detail and methods implemented to avoid these problems in the future.

Project:	Date:
Location:	Project Manager:
Comm. No:	General Contractor:
Client:	Completion Date:

	Yes	No	Unk
1. Was the client happy with the final results of the project?	____	____	____
2. On a scale of 1 to 10, 1 being poor and 10 being excellent, rate how we perceive the client's satisfaction.	1 2 3 4 5 6 7 8 9 10		
3. Will this client use us again in the future?	____	____	____
4. Will this client recommend us to others?	____	____	____
5. Was the firm happy with the final results of the project?	____	____	____
6. On a scale of 1 to 10, rate how satisfied the firm was with the project.	1 2 3 4 5 6 7 8 9 10		
7. Is this project worthy of publication and/or suitable to be photographed and displayed in our office gallery?	____	____	____
8. Was the firm happy with architect/client relationship?	____	____	____
9. Did the client pay his bills on time?	____	____	____
10. Would the firm want to do work with this client again?	____	____	____
11. Was the staff strained to meet deadlines?	____	____	____
12. Did the staff enjoy working on the project?	____	____	____
13. Was this project completed within the allotted time schedule?	____	____	____

Exhibit 12 Completed Project Evaluation Form (continued)

	Yes	No	Unk
14. Was the project profitable to the firm?	_____	_____	_____
15. Was the performance of the outside consultants satisfactory?	_____	_____	_____
16. Rate the consultants used on a scale of 1 to 10 in reference to their performance:			
A. Structural	1 2 3 4 5 6 7 8 9 10		
B. Mechanical	1 2 3 4 5 6 7 8 9 10		
C. Electrical	1 2 3 4 5 6 7 8 9 10		
D. Civil	1 2 3 4 5 6 7 8 9 10		
17. Was the contractor's performance satisfactory?	_____	_____	_____
18. Rate the contractor's overall total job performance on a scale of 1 to 10.	1 2 3 4 5 6 7 8 9 10		
19. Could the firm recommend this contractor to future clients?	_____	_____	_____
20. Did the contractor try to generate unnecessary change orders?	_____	_____	_____
21. Did the contractor try to shift any of his responsibility to the architect?	_____	_____	_____
22. Did the contractor submit shop drawings that were not required by our specifications?	_____	_____	_____
23. Did the contractor ever try to dilute the architect's authority by going to the owner directly with proposed substitutions or design changes?	_____	_____	_____
24. Did problems arise on the job that the staff can now learn and benefit from and not repeat in the future?	_____	_____	_____
25. Did any ambiguities in the contract documents develop that can be avoided in the future?	_____	_____	_____

simple, answering the basic question: Where is your firm headed and who will help you get there?

Start by thinking about your firm's short-term and long-term goals. What kind of work do you expect to do, now and in the future? Do you have enough people with the proper expertise to tackle tasks at hand as well as anticipated work? What standards of service, quality and ethics do you want to maintain? Having a clear picture of the answers to these questions will guide you in selecting the right professionals to meet your organizational needs.

Your employees are a large part of your firm's public image. Think hard about the caliber of the people you want representing you to your clients. If you seek high-quality professionals (and you should), create high standards. If you want imaginative people who can grow and change as your firm grows and changes, create the kind of environment that will satisfy and nurture them. Only planning and foresight will make that happen. Once you determine what you, as a firm, represent, and the kind of people you need, employee recruitment and selection will be easier.

Recruitment and Selection

When a clear job description is in place, you can begin your search for qualified candidates. Recruitment techniques vary. You can find good people through advertising, referrals from your peers, recruiting firms and campus recruitment. Many firms find that the most effective way to identify likely candidates is through referrals from their staff, and they create incentives for such referrals.

Before you interview, make certain you are current on state and federal employment laws and regulations. Your responsibilities as an employer or potential employer are far-ranging, encompassing wages, equal employment opportunity, affirmative action, immigration, fair labor standards and other issues. Make someone in your firm responsible for keeping up-to-date on human resources regulations. If you don't have the expertise in-house, your attorney or professional association can steer you in the right direction.

Once you have solicited resumés and narrowed down the field of candidates, an interview will allow you to ask the questions mere resumés and letters can't answer. During the interview, you have the opportunity to go beyond technical qualifications and find out about the applicant's interests and motivations. Is he the type of individual who will work well with the other members of your firm? Is she flexible and open to feedback? Can he cope with changes and the complexities of the job? Is she sincerely interested in your firm and its goals? Is he just looking for another job or does he want the opportunity to make a substantial contribution to your firm? Does she have the interpersonal skills necessary to work with your clients and other members of your team? Evaluate each candidate on the basis of all the factors you consider necessary to successfully fill the job. It is helpful to use a matrix or scoring sheet to organize your questions, especially when you are interviewing several candidates for a position.

A successful hiring decision is a two-way street: the employee gets a chance to select you, too. Be certain to explain the requirements of the position you are trying to fill. Be prepared to talk about what your firm has to offer. Whether it is growth potential, challenging projects or more individuality and creativity, pinpoint what makes your firm special and why you are an attractive employer. Allow candidates to tell you what they're looking for. Will your organization meet their needs?

Check your candidates' references. You can verify what you've learned about the prospective employee by telephoning former employers and associates. While people are often reluctant to put negative information on paper, they may be willing to tell you about a candidate's competency in a telephone conversation. This is also a good time to confirm some of your initial impressions. Ask open-ended questions; these individuals may have just the information you need to make the right decision.

Every hiring decision is a calculated risk. You can never be sure that the screening, interviewing and selection process will produce a successful on-the-job professional. The odds are in your favor, however, if you manage to keep a balanced, objective perspective.

Employee Orientation

Because your firm operates like no other, a new member to your firm — no matter how experienced — will need some basic orientation to your organization. His or her future effectiveness can depend on a clear understanding of your firm's policies and procedures.

Explain to your new employee how he or she will fit into your organization. Prepare a simple company handbook for all your employees that explains the firm's history, organizational procedures, employee benefits, lines of communication and other important details. In addition, you will want to familiarize your new employee with your clients and their concerns. Pass along any information that will help the newcomer perform more effectively.

This is the time, too, to have a new hire review the loss prevention strategies discussed in this book. In particular, have him or her review the sections that deal with professionalism, effective communication with clients and his or her duties in the event of a conflict or incident. (In fact, many firms use this book as a loss prevention primer for all personnel.) Make certain your employees understand safety procedures and their jobsite responsibilities.

Finally, early in the new hire's employment, check the quality and competence of his or her work, particularly technical work, to ensure that they in
fact have the required skills and knowledge.

Professional Development

No two design professionals, presented with the same complex design
problem, will produce identical solutions. Although both solutions may be
workable, carefully drafted and unambiguous, there may be distinct
differences between them from a professional liability standpoint. One of the
designs may be far more likely to cause a claim. Obviously, the competence
of the contractor can make a big difference. But, to a great extent, design
judgment, or the lack of it, determines the degree of claims exposure
encountered on a project.

What constitutes good design judgment? It is sometimes defined as the
ability to evaluate alternatives and recommend an optimum solution to a
design problem — not only from an artistic or technical point of view, but
from a practical standpoint as well — constructibility, project cost, operating
cost, sustainability and maintainability.

How can you help your employees improve their design judgment? Solid
academic training plays a large part in developing sound design judgment.
But so does a wide range of on-the-job experience, particularly when
combined with in-house education. A very valuable form of in-house
education is a *mentorship*, in which a relatively inexperienced project staff
person is coached by a more experienced design professional in a one-on-
one relationship. Some firms hold in-house meetings in which seasoned
veterans relate their "war stories" about design problems or professional
liability claims for younger professionals in the firm. Other firms like to
conduct regular project evaluations or case studies to illustrate what went

right and, just as importantly, what went wrong with an assignment. Many firms offer in-house programs that include seminars led by senior principals, subconsultants, attorneys, insurance brokers, management consultants or product representatives.

There are also many opportunities for continuing education outside the firm. Those with weak technical education will need more formalized help, since their lack of skills may lead to persistent technical errors. Some architects and engineers pursue advanced or additional university degrees. Professional societies have also developed numerous seminars and courses to help their members keep up with new technologies and business practices. Information from these societies as well as professional journals can be extremely helpful. Establish a system to make such information available to your staff. Often, design firms encourage their employees' efforts to enhance their skills by paying for all or part of the tuition or seminar fees.

The quest for new technical knowledge should never stop. Because design professionals are expected to remain reasonably informed about the technical developments in their discipline, on-going education and the encouragement of high quality design judgment might be a matter of professional survival.

Employee Motivation

Good companies foster good feelings among their people. The surest way to have a staff functioning at its best is to create an environment where everyone has the opportunity to succeed. This means allowing your firm's professionals to set goals and find their own ways to achieve them. Nothing motivates like feeling in control of the decision-making process. Whenever possible, provide your professionals with the autonomy they need to do their work to the best of their abilities. Challenge them, but provide a context in which they can safely meet these challenges. Trust the talent, intelligence and expertise of the people you hire, and you'll probably get the results you want.

Even in the most positive environment, individual efforts will vary. What motivates people to give their best differs from person to person. For many, financial compensation is not enough. Most people need recognition, too, in the form of a promotion, praise, peer recognition or challenging assignments. Some want the chance to contribute to the community or to enhance their professional reputation. Some need to work alone; many want to work on a good team.

In general, a firm that wants to motivate its employees encourages new ideas, pays a fair salary with competitive benefits, acknowledges and rewards individual contributions, encourages employees to see the "big picture" and provides for professional growth. It "plays fair" with its employees and doesn't subject them to the whims of a capricious management. It works hard to discover the employees' gifts and individual needs and, in so doing, helps them get all they can out of their careers.

A firm that truly motivates its employees refuses to squander their talents and resources. This is also an important loss prevention measure. Occasional overtime or a crisis deadline for which everyone must pull together to get the job done is expected in professional service and can be a healthy, team building experience. When crash projects and excessive overtime become the norm, however, employees become fatigued and begin to make errors. Tempers flare and attention to quality begins to slip. The result can be omissions, oversights, failures, claims — and the loss of a valuable employee who views constant "fire drills" as a sign of poor management.

Instead, learn to use your firm's personnel effectively. Make certain you schedule your projects efficiently and, if the workload is occasionally too heavy but does not warrant additional hires, bring in contract workers or temporary employees to handle the extra work rather than wear out your firm's best assets.

Keep your ear to the ground. Encourage your employees to tell you how they feel about the level of effort you ask of them, their fatigue factor, their health and their attitudes about their assignments. If your interest is sincere, your employees will appreciate your concern — and you just might learn a great deal about managing your firm.

Moonlighting Employees

Do any of your employees hold a second job with another design firm or perform professional work for others on the side? This could get you into serious trouble. Almost without exception, employees who accept outside work don't bother to carry professional liability insurance and are often unaware of the risks of liability, both to themselves *and* their employers.

Why do employees moonlight, after all? The major reason is financial — to supplement their basic salary. Since most projects that involve moonlighting have limited scopes and budgets, the possibility of litigation is extremely high. Because you, the employer, usually have greater assets, it would not be unusual for an enterprising lawyer to include you in a lawsuit as a deep pocket. Unfair as it sounds, plaintiffs have used the argument that the moonlighter's employer derived some benefit from the employee's moonlighting, since the firm would not otherwise be able to afford the employee. A damaged plaintiff could also claim he or she thought the employer was involved or at least condoned the moonlighting. Since the plaintiff would call the employee at his or her regular job with questions or

119

receive some sketches that were on company letterhead, it appeared the company was fully knowledgeable and was a party to the work. Although you might not be brought into the litigation, the employee is subjected to the mental and emotional anxiety of a lawsuit which will most likely interfere with productivity.

Even if no lawsuit is pending, there is always the risk of deterioration in the quality and amount of work a moonlighting employee can perform during the regular working day. Psychologists tell us that the average individual is capable of a limited amount of productivity in any given time span. If this productive effort is expended on something other than regular employment, the employer is deprived of the employee's best efforts. Usually, fatigue results and the probability of mistakes skyrockets.

Moonlighting by your employees should be prohibited or strictly controlled by written company policy. Many firm's policies prohibit moonlighting without the express consent of a managing principal — and consent is rarely given. This policy is agreed to and signed by all employees.

It may be that your employees are unaware of the risks involved with moonlighting. It is up to you to explain why it is unacceptable. If they understand that they put not only themselves but their jobs and their employer in jeopardy by accepting outside work, they may be less tempted to agree to design that recreation room for their brother-in-law's friend.

Business Management

Of all the skills expected of design firm managers and entrepreneurs, many architects and engineers find they are least prepared for the business side of their practice. Yet these skills are every bit as important as their technical competence. For instance, the management staffs of leading industrial companies are usually weighted heavily on the business side, with MBAs and law degrees, while the engineering and production people make up a relatively small portion of the staff. Design firms can learn from this model. Often, the best solution to management shortcomings is to hire a professional manager. A business manager can add needed expertise in such areas as contracts, negotiations, expense control, collections monitoring and capital management. Combining business talent with technical competence creates an extremely efficient decision-making team.

The positioning of the business manager within the firm is very important. Companies dominated by technical or production-oriented people often founder, while those that position their business managers on the same organizational level as their technical and production personnel are more successful. Remember that the successful business is a multi-dimensional unit. All dimensions must be in balance if that unit is to remain stable. The design firm that emphasizes the design aspects over the business considerations of the practice may not be a well-balanced company.

The design professional firm that is too small to afford a full-time manager should consider employing a part-time business manager. If this is not possible, the firm must ask its principals to assume the additional responsibilities. They will find themselves managing personnel and accounting, developing new business, attending professional society seminars and dealing with equipment repair persons. Each principal should assume the staff functions most compatible with his or her personality and abilities.

The principals should also try to get the proper training in basic business principles. This takes commitment in a busy practice, yet to maximize profit — and reduce professional liability claims — they must spend time developing the skills needed to make appropriate business decisions. Several

121

organizations provide help in developing management skills, including the American Management Association and the Small Business Administration. The ACEC, AIA, ASCE and NSPE all have books, courses and staff available to help. In addition, most universities and community colleges offer business management courses.

Peer Reviews

A superb way to constructively examine the management and business operations of your firm is through an organizational peer review. The American Consulting Engineers Council (ACEC) has developed such a program, which is also endorsed by The American Institute of Architects (AIA). Conducted by trained, qualified peers, the review provides a confidential look at the general management, professional development, project management, human resources management, financial management and business development of each firm. Firms that have participated in a peer review are overwhelmingly positive about the experience. In one architect's words: "I am even more convinced that it has had a significant impact on our firm. We got the input we needed at a critical time, and also have a clearer understanding of who we are, who we want to be, and where we are going."[1]

Summary

- The business side of a design firm requires just as much attention and expertise as the technical side.

- Learn to identify and manage all the potential risks on a project.

- Client evaluation is a key risk management exercise.

- Insist on a fair fee for your services.

- The best method of procurement for design services is qualifications based selection (QBS).

- Make certain your firm has the capability to provide the services for which it advertises and contracts.

- Work with your client to develop a carefully defined scope of services that sets forth those services you will provide, as well as those you will not.

- A well-drafted, fair and reasonably protective contract is absolutely essential when providing design services.

- Try to include a limitation of liability clause in every contract.

- Make sure your contract with your client is clear on how and when you will be paid, as well as your rights in the event of nonpayment; be diligent about invoicing and follow-up.

- Providing cost estimates or promising to deliver plans and specifications by a certain date often gives rise to claims.

- Both prime and subconsultants need to carefully evaluate each other before entering into a contract.

- The selection, training and retention of personnel is one of your firm's most important management issues.

- Many successful firms hire business managers to help them address contractual, financial and personnel issues.

[1]H. Kennard Bussard, FAIA. *Communiqué*, September, 1993.

C

12

TECHNICAL PROCEDURES

During the last few years, there has been a great deal of fascination given to quality improvement methodologies. However varied and complex some of these methods may be, they share a common theme. It is simply this: The success of your practice rests on the commitment to quality at every level of your firm. All your employees must understand that the firm's livelihood (and consequently their own) depends on delivering high-caliber service that meets the client's expectations while earning the firm a fair profit.

0   9o   100 Metres

A Commitment to Quality

Such a philosophy must be driven and inspired by your firm's principals. They, in turn, must instill in employees the importance of striving to do the job right the first time; they must lead the effort for constant quality improvement. Regardless of the size of your firm, the fundamentals don't change. On every job, an emphasis on teamwork and communication, a clear definition of project requirements and the use of standard, well-conceived procedures will produce a higher quality of service and enhance your client's satisfaction.

The commitment to quality you bring to the technical aspects of your job directly affects your firm's exposure to risk. The attention you pay to details — in your strict procedures for specification checking, for instance, and in your handling of the bid period and construction phase services — can make all the difference between a practice that is successful and a practice that is constantly fending off claims.

The Design Phase

Drawings

One of the primary means of communicating with the contractor is through your drawings. Of all the design documents, the drawings are referred to most frequently; they are the graphic representation of your instructions to the contractor and must be as complete, coordinated, easy to follow and as error-free as possible. Often, the construction worker at the jobsite is given a set of drawings but never sees the specifications. Even if specifications are available, a worker usually prefers the visual plan of work — the drawings.

Drawings should be neat, legible and arranged in logical sequence. Scaling and dimensioning should be appropriate. Some firms show dimensions, quantities or capacities in only one place on the drawings. That way, necessary changes are made just once and the likelihood of conflicting information is reduced.

Notes and symbols clarify your drawings. There are many standard symbols, but if your firm develops its own or uses variations of the standard symbols, be sure to explain their meaning both in a symbol legend on the drawings and in a standard definitions section of the General Conditions. In general, limit the notes on the drawings to the minimum necessary to show your intent. References to quality and workmanship belong in the specifications.

The relationship of the drawings to the specifications must *always* be considered — the two documents should supplement and reinforce each other. Coordinate designations on the drawings with those used in the specifications. Check for and eliminate conflicts between the drawings and the specifications.

To check their drawings, many firms use design checklists. These most often take the form of a list of categories or processes applicable to a particular design specialty. They contain items common to every project using that particular design, and other items less frequently used but of importance to some specific projects. (A portion of a typical design checklist is shown in *Exhibit 13.*) If used properly, design checklists make it less likely that you will omit a required item.

In addition to having consistent checking methodology, firms that have fewer claims tend to use *design manuals.* Although you can find general information about a particular type of system or method in industry reference materials, manufacturers' bulletins and test data, an office design manual gives you a step-by-step description of the design methods used to develop the

127

Exhibit 13   Design Checklist Sample Page

Design Checklist

Expert & Sage, Inc.
Consulting Engineers
3424 Michigan Avenue
Chicago, IL 60654

3. Outdoor Conditions - Cold Weather Design
   Rain and Snow Design - Ventilation Louvers

ITEMS (continued)
Checked by:

c. Are the outside air intake louvers located above normal snow collection or drift line?   _____

d. Are the "storm-proof" louver blades specified on outside air intake louvers?   _____

e. Is a proper drainage method shown on drawing detail to permit moisture carry-over to drain from louver and from any connecting ductwork?   _____

f. Does the outside air intake louver specified have low enough air velocity at design air quantity to prevent moisture carry-over?   _____

g. Are the outside air intake and exhaust air louvers located other than facing into prevailing wind?   _____

h. Check air friction pressure drop across all louvers at design air quantities and design velocities. (File copy of catalog selection chart of each manufacturer specified and mark design point on chart or curve.)   _____

drawings for a specific type of system and reflects the special preferences of your firm.

Create a design manual by having your most qualified people outline the best procedures used in designing a system or method. You should include standard calculations forms and samples of actual calculations performed on a project, as well as items or procedures repeatedly encountered on projects where this particular design is used. When a design manual is completed and in use, it should be considered a "living" document. Each project manager, in turn, should note design improvements, field problems and corrections, or other helpful information gained through experience, and have the information promptly added to the manual. Some firms now keep their design manuals on computers, making it easier to call up the firm's latest standard design procedures and make necessary revisions. If your manual is not on computer, make sure that updates are issued regularly to all manual users. (See *Exhibit 14* for a sample page of a design manual.)

129

Some firms develop standard details that show their preferred methods of assembly or arrangement and reproduce them on transparent stick-ons, which are then attached to the final drawings. These firms reason that since standard details typically show their best design solutions, using them saves design and drafting time and, more importantly, limits the possibility of drafting errors.

You must, however, exercise caution and professional judgment when using standard details. Although useful and efficient, standard details can be troublesome. Sometimes they are improperly used, or errors or omissions result when they are tied to the rest of the design. If you use standard details, apply them *only* when they are appropriate. *Never* alter your design requirements to fit a standard detail. Properly applied, standard details can serve you well; misapplied, they can get you into a lot of trouble.

Exhibit 14   Design Manual Sample Page

Design Manual

Expert & Sage, Inc.
Consulting Engineers
3424 Michigan Avenue
Chicago, IL 60654

Air Conditioning

B. CHILLED WATER COOLING AND SPRAYED COIL AND SINGLE DUCT, LOW VELOCITY, HOT WATER REHEAT SYSTEM (continued)

3. Counterflow Piping Connections - Hot Water Coils

a.   *Always* design the hot water piping connections to hot water reheat coils to produce *counterflow* between the air and water; the entering hot water connection *must* be on the leaving air side of the coil, and the leaving hot water connection *must* be on the entering air side of the coil.

b.   It is preferred that the leaving water connection be located at a higher elevation than the entering water connection to facilitate air bubble elimination, but this design consideration is *not* as important as having counterflow connections.

4. Piping and Connections - Hot Water Coils

a.   Detail the piping connections to a typical hot water reheat coil *only once* on the drawings. Each exception to the typical detail must be reviewed individually by requiring submittal of shop drawings for review.

b.   The standard typical isometric detail of piping connections to a horizontal air flow hot water reheat coil was carefully designed to provide the minimum number of joints in piping and fitting and still provide sufficient means of expansion and contraction in the piping. *Use this detail! Do not* attempt to design one yourself without first checking with your supervisor.

c.   All hot water reheat coil piping accessories, such as thermometer wells, shut-off and balancing values, etc., are shown on standard typical detail of hot water reheat coil No. HC-IX.

5. Selection of Hot Water Reheat Coils

a.   When hot water reheat coils are selected for location in ductwork running in the ceiling space over occupied areas designed under rigid acoustical criteria, ...

130

Today, almost every design firm has some computer-aided design and drafting (CADD) capability. Such systems can reduce the risk of conflicts, errors and omissions, ensure standard dimensioning and lettering throughout the document and produce clear, easy to read drawings. CADD software requires a good deal of training for your firm's staff, though, and it is important to understand that these programs are not foolproof. Because something is computer-generated does not mean it is correct. Make certain an experienced staff member reviews any new CADD software and, once it is installed, reviews all your CADD-generated documents. Remember, as advantageous as CADD is, it is not always an appropriate substitute for manual drafting. There are still many instances where circumstance, time, money and aesthetics call for a human touch.

Specifications

Specifications depict in words the requirements for the materials, construction systems, equipment, standards and workmanship necessary to construct what the design professional has drawn. Combined with drawings and other contract documents, specifications enable contractors to develop bids for submission to the owner. Most often, specifications are contained in the project manual, along with the bidding requirements, contract forms, and the general and special conditions of the contract.

Of all the sections of the contract documents, the specifications section is probably the least respected — by design professionals and contractors alike. Certainly, design professionals devote too little time and care to their development. Perhaps this is because designers often regard specifications writing as a nuisance and prefer the more creative work involving drawings and calculations. Or perhaps it is because too few architects and engineers are really comfortable with the special skill necessary to write accurate specifications. Regardless, design professionals must understand that *specifications are every bit as important as drawings.* Keep in mind that should you be involved in litigation arising from one of your projects, the courts will be more likely to refer to your specifications than to your drawings to discover your intent, simply because it is easier for a layperson to understand written descriptions than graphic depictions.

A significant number of professional liability claims can be traced back to faulty specifications. The culprits tend to be ambiguous text, lack of coordination and the failure of some specified items to meet performance or design requirements.

Effective specifications writing requires the skill of well-qualified personnel who adhere to proven methodologies and conventions. An inconsistent, hit-or-miss approach to specifications writing can easily lead to conflicts among the various sections of the specifications and drawings or to omission of items critical to the project.

In Chapter Two, we explained the importance of using precise language in specifications. Make certain that the words you use to describe a specific item are the same throughout the documents. This consistency is particularly important when you are trying to establish a relationship between requirements in the specifications and the same item on the drawings. Use only recognizable symbols and numerals. Avoid abbreviations and acronyms, unless they are widely accepted and defined in the documents. Remember, to people outside the construction industry — and even to some within it — the words that designers use can seem like a foreign language. Therefore, include a definition of terms section in every set of specifications or in the General Conditions. Define all words, terms or acronyms that have a special meaning or more than one meaning.

A good way to avoid specifications omissions is to use a specification checklist and a drawing coordination checklist. Often, architects and engineers use a *master specification* and modify it for each project. Many rely on published master specifications, such as those developed by the Construction Standards Institute (CSI) or AIA's MASTERSPEC. Most master specifications are organized in the conventional sixteen-section format, and almost all can be used with word processing software. Whatever checklist your firm decides upon, be sure it is used consistently and thoroughly; it is useful only if it is completely filled out and reviewed.

All too often, the writing of specifications begins too late in a project. It is best to begin developing the specifications during design development. Then, by the time the drawings are developed, the specifications are fairly well thought out. Many firms believe that the person selecting the materials, products or systems for the project should be involved in developing the specifications. If the person doing the design is not adept at specifications writing (some good designers are just not "word" people), then, at the very least, have the designer and the specifications writer work closely together.

Some firms prefer to rely on specifications consultants. Such consultants can be valuable because of their extensive technical knowledge, their expertise in the conventions of specifications writing and their familiarity with materials and systems. Unfortunately, specifications consultants are often retained too late in the design process and are forced to develop the specifications when the drawings are complete and the schedule is too tight. The result: an increased likelihood that an important detail will be overlooked. If your firm retains a specifications consultant, he or she should be brought in no later than the early stages of the construction document phase.

Specifying Materials and Products

Architecture and engineering are not exact sciences. Although you specify what you believe are the best or most appropriate components, trouble sometimes occurs. If a claim arises from the failure of a material or product, the injured party usually sues the design professional along with the contractor and the manufacturer. People unfamiliar with the construction industry often think you have complete knowledge of the manufactured products you specify. They may assume you research and test each item or system before specifying its use. If such a case goes to trial, you will have difficulty proving that you were not negligent when you specified an inappropriate or faulty product. After all, a jury may reason, you are the design *professional.*

Many projects you design have an experimental element to them, because the exact combination of systems and materials probably has never been designed and built before. This aspect of the profession makes it hazardous enough; do not place yourself at further risk by specifying unproven new products or familiar products in untried applications. Whenever possible, make it a practice to specify products or components that have been thoroughly tested and have been tried and proved effective in your particular application.

If you are determined to specify new materials or components that are untried in your application, you must do your homework. You are expected to be at least reasonably knowledgeable about new technology and developments in your profession. Research the latest information on all materials you specify and document your research efforts. Contact the manufacturer to get details about other projects in which the product has been used and ask for all technical data, warranties and product literature. Don't rely on promotional or marketing brochures. Inform the manufacturer — in writing — how you intend to use the product and, if appropriate, require the manufacturer to warrant in writing that the product is appropriate for the intended application. You may even want to require a representative of the manufacturer to be on site during installation to be sure the product is properly applied or installed.

If your client insists — against your better judgment — that you specify materials you are uncertain about, take strong precautions. If the product is experimental in nature and successful performance is questionable, persuade the owner to inspect other, similar installations and/or agree to a test program. Make your client an integral part of the process — and let him or her assume the risk involved. Ask the advice of your attorney regarding contractual protection from the risks of being directed to specify untried materials or products.

You should never agree to specify a product you believe represents a potential risk to public health or safety. If your client insists on something you feel is unsafe, document your objections in the strongest terms possible, and, if he or she is still insistent, walk away from the project.

Between conservatism and highly experimental design lies safe ground. Look for it as though your future depends on it. It does.

Documenting Your Design Decisions

As we mentioned in Chapter Two, it is important to document in writing the details of any meetings or discussions held regarding the project. The same holds true for your design decisions. What were the circumstances or factors that led you to a given decision? For the purposes of checking and backchecking — and in the event of a question later on — you should be able to show the assumptions underlying your design, the criteria you used and the calculations that were performed.

135

You will also want to document the various design alternatives available and the reasons you selected one over another. Under the professional standard of care for your discipline, you may well have a duty to investigate or discuss those alternatives with your client. Also keep track of the decisions, directives or requests of others. It is important to be able to show the recommendations of a manufacturer or a code interpretation by a public official.

Finally, carefully track your client's role in the decision-making process — especially those decisions that conflict with your recommendations. If your client doesn't agree with your aesthetic judgment, that's one thing; you may just have to bite your tongue and let the client have his or her way. You cannot, however, knowingly violate building codes, even at your client's request. If public health and safety are at stake, it's a different ball game. No matter where you practice, your duty to safeguard the public overrides any obligation to the client. You must advise your client of the situation (documenting your actions) and if he or she fails to take appropriate action, alert the appropriate authorities.

Coordinating the Documents

Coordinating the documents of all your subconsultants and the other design disciplines is a critical task. The point of interface between two or more disciplines is the source of many design errors and omissions. Establish a careful, systematic approach to this effort in order to ensure a fully coordinated and consistent set of construction documents. You need to review the documents to make certain that all items shown on the drawings are specified and that the engineering systems will fit in the physical areas designed for them. Details, schedules, elevations and sections must agree with each other.

Coordination is a job for highly skilled and experienced employees. Very often, however, less experienced people are assigned to do the final coordination review. Worse, project managers may wait until the last minute to consolidate drawings from the other disciplines. The result: too little or no coordination review — and probably a claim.

Professional societies for architects and engineers have developed worthwhile publications that deal with quality control in the preparation of working drawings, specifications and document coordination; their addresses are listed in the Bibliography.

An Aggressive Approach to Error Detection

Even in the most quality oriented firm, plans and specifications can contain discrepancies or deficiencies that will lead to requests for information (RFIs) or require corrections or change orders.

Inexperienced owners may expect design professionals to produce flawless design documents. Design professionals know that there is no such thing as a perfect set of plans, but hesitate to raise this issue with the owner. For your protection, however, this discussion *must* take place. (This is one reason why partnering is such a good idea. You, the client and the contractor can openly discuss anticipated problems and decide in advance how to deal with them when they arise. For more information, see the discussion of partnering in Chapter Three.)

One large architectural/engineering firm handles the issue in this way: It begins with the realistic premise that construction documents *will* require further development that *will* cause change orders to be written (and create additional project costs). It explains this to the client and secures the client's acknowledgment. The firm calls attention to the fact that good practice allows for a certain amount of leeway in development as the project moves

137

from final design toward actual construction. It explains to the owner that the project will not be final until after construction is completed — that the project *will evolve and improve* as time passes.

The firm also makes a commitment to identify and address conflicts, omissions, code violations, errors and improper use of materials as early as possible. It mitigates such problems by contractually obligating all participants in the construction process — suppliers, subcontractors and contractors — to advise the owner and the design firm of any deficiency they know about. The firm specifies a date (before work commences) for contractors, subcontractors and vendors to file a notice describing any discrepancies they have discovered and their suggested solutions.

Although the majority of discrepancies will be discovered during construction, these procedures also help provide early warning signals of potential problems. Timing is critical: the sooner the discrepancy can be identified, the sooner it can be remedied and the less it will cost to correct.

During the construction phase, this same firm holds weekly project meetings to review the construction schedule and the submittals needing review and clarification. The agenda always includes the reiteration that one of the purposes of the meeting is to identify at the earliest moment conflicts, errors, omissions, code violations or improper use of materials. This creates a receptive climate that is effective in stimulating early and cost-effective problem resolution. Such a discussion helps to get individual egos out of the way and fosters an atmosphere in which everyone wants to help get problems solved. It is refreshing, contractors and clients say, to have people admit they are not infallible.

Finally, but most importantly, the firm discusses with the owner the inevitability of changes in the design and asks that a contingency fund be set aside to cover the cost of these changes. This is done by including an appropriate clause in the contract. (This firm often suggests a contingency of 3-5 percent of the construction budget. Every project is different, however, and a higher or lower percentage may be more appropriate. Just make certain the figure you use is realistic.)

By following these steps, this design firm ensures that the owner has realistic expectations about the potential costs associated with design errors or omissions.

This firm has an enviable record, with few disputes or claims over the years. There have been errors and there have been problems — every complex project has its share. However, with realistic expectations, early error detection, good project team communication, a receptive attitude and an appropriate contingency for design problems, difficulties rarely escalate into conflicts, disputes or claims.

The Construction Bid Period

The way you respond to Requests for Clarification by bidders just before bids are due is particularly important. Although few problems arise when there is sufficient time to issue a written addendum and to make sure it reaches everyone involved, costly complications can result if you depart from this well-established procedure.

Has this ever happened in your practice? A contractor, subcontractor or material supplier who is rushing to assemble bid figures calls your office for last-minute interpretations of your drawings and specifications. In an effort to be helpful, your employee verbally clarifies an apparent ambiguity, not realizing there is insufficient time before bid closing to issue the same

139

clarification to all potential bidders. Consequently, one bidder gains an unfair competitive advantage over the others. Or, conversely, the answer given under time pressure turns out to be wrong, and one bidder ultimately suffers a significant disadvantage.

Telephone information given to contractors during bidding is a continuing source of claims. Instruct your personnel to refrain from giving verbal interpretations of drawings or specifications, even if the contractor points out an obvious error. Instead, send written addenda to all contractors bidding — if there is time before bids are due. Spell out methods in the bid documents by which the contractor may qualify the bid if clarifications by addenda are unavailable. Then, when questions do arise, you can refer the contractor to the bid documents for the proper procedures to use. Of course, subconsultants should be instructed *not* to answer bidders' questions directly. Information must pass from the subconsultant to the prime design professional, who can then pass it on to bidders. The prime architect or engineer must maintain control of and document all information given to bidders.

Some design professionals post a notice next to each telephone in the company's drafting room to help employees handle bid-related questions. (See *Exhibit 15* for a typical notice.)

Other design professionals approach this problem by warning bidding contractors and subcontractors not to use unauthorized data when calculating their bids. One design professional sends bidders a carefully drafted letter of explanation similar to the one on page 143, with a copy of a statement they will be required to execute. (See *Bidder's Representation, Exhibit 16.*)

Exhibit 15 Bid Period Communications

EMPLOYEE NOTICE

If you receive a telephone call or a personal visit from a contractor, subcontractor or material supplier during the bid period on a project, and he or she asks for a clarification or interpretation, contending there is an error or ambiguity on the drawings or specifications — DO NOT VOLUNTEER YOUR OWN OPINION NO MATTER HOW CONVINCED YOU ARE THAT YOU KNOW THE ANSWER! INSTEAD, DO THE FOLLOWING:

1. Instruct the caller to conform to the instructions contained in General Conditions on Instruction to Bidders. If the caller persists, ask your department head to handle the situation.

2. If the department head is not available and the caller insists on an immediate answer, respond as follows:

a. Carefully write down the content of the caller's request and his or her assertions as to what and why some portions of the drawings or specifications are ambiguous or in error. (*Do not express your opinion as to whether or not the caller is correct.*)

b. Tell the caller you *cannot* provide pertinent information because it may give the caller a competitive advantage not enjoyed by others bidding or quoting on the project.

c. Inform the caller that you will pass the request for information to your department head but that any clarification, correction or change in the drawings or specifications must be issued in the form of a written addendum.

d. If there appears to be insufficient time to issue an addendum, tell the caller you cannot give information verbally and that, based on the content of the drawings and specifications as they are, without any assistance from you, pending issuance of an addendum or a possible extension of the bid period, the caller must arrive at his or her own conclusions.

Exhibit 16   Bidder's Representation

Bidder's Representation

By the act of submitting a bid for the proposed contract, the Bidder represents that:

- The Bidder and all subcontractors the Bidder intends to use have carefully and thoroughly reviewed the drawings, specifications and other construction documents and have found them complete and free from ambiguities and sufficient for the purpose intended.
- The Bidder and all workers, employees and subcontractors the Bidder intends to use are skilled and experienced in the type of construction represented by the construction contract documents bid upon.
- The bid figure is based solely upon the construction contract documents and properly issued written addenda and not upon any other written representation.
- Neither the Bidder nor any of the Bidder's employees, agents, intended suppliers or subcontractors have relied upon any verbal representations from the Owner, or the Owner's employees or agents including architects, engineers or consultants, in assembling the bid figure.

   Acknowledged:

     By: _____

     For: _____

     Date: _____

As the client's representative, we would like to point out one especially important provision of the construction contract documents, the Bidder's Representation (extra copy enclosed).

Your careful reading of the Bidder's Representation is imperative because, by signing and submitting it with your bid figure, you will be representing to the owner that 1) your detailed examination of the drawings and specifications has turned up no ambiguities which need clarification, 2) only authorized data have been used to arrive at your bid figure, and 3) the experience and capabilities of your firm, your workers and your subcontractors are adequate and appropriate to perform the construction of this type of project.

Please note that each of your subcontractors will also be required to submit a signed copy of the Bidder's Representation before the owner can award the construction contract.

If you find that you are unable to sign this representation because you believe the drawings or specifications are inadequate or erroneous in some way, please notify us at once so that corrective action can be taken. Similarly, if your bid figure is affected by information not contained in the construction contract documents, contact us immediately before submitting your bid.

143

Note that the above letter accomplishes another important matter: it obligates the contractor to report any defects he or she discovers in the contract documents. (See *An Aggressive Approach to Error Detection*, page 137.)

No matter how you decide to handle bid period procedures, discuss the matter with your attorney in the event that case law or statutes in your jurisdiction require special protections.

The Construction Phase

One of the most potent loss prevention measures at your disposal is the scope of construction phase services you agree to in your contract with your client. It is important that you be hired to observe the work to determine if it is in general conformance with the construction documents, to review shop drawings and other appropriate submittals, to provide interpretation of the plans to the contractors and, if necessary, to be involved in suggesting ways to mitigate any problems arising in the contract documents.

Of course, construction phase duties can differ from project to project and discipline to discipline. If you are the prime design professional on a project, you may be called upon to provide a more comprehensive construction contract administration service, to process contractor requests for payment and to administer the completion and close-out process for the owner. If a continuous on-site presence is required, a full-time project representative might be in order. On the other hand, it is just as important for subconsultants to provide construction phase services that relate to their portion of the design.

Whatever construction phase duties you and your client agree upon, make certain that your scope of services is very clear and that you will be paid for the services you provide. It is also a good idea to specify in your contract what services you will *not* be providing — those services to be excluded. (See page 85.) Make sure, too, that your responsibilities — and those that will remain with the contractor or someone else — are reflected in the General Conditions of the owner's agreement with the contractor.

Construction Observation

The best way to assure that the project is being built in general conformance with the contract documents and according to the design concept is to visit the project site. Design questions or ambiguities in the plans or specifications can be interpreted in the field and problems can be caught and resolved early, at minimum expense.

Construction observation should be included in your scope of services for every project. Your contract should provide for visits at appropriate intervals to the project site to conduct visual observation of materials and completed work and to determine if the work is proceeding in general conformance with the information given in the contract documents and with the design concept.

The design professional's "observation" role on the project site is often misunderstood, however. Many clients (to say nothing of juries) do not understand that, unlike inspection, construction observation is quite limited in scope and purpose. The difference between inspection and observation can be crucial. For instance, it is a common misconception that the purpose of your observation is to "inspect" the contractor's work to uncover any code violations or defects in the construction. "Inspection" implies that you will monitor all the contractor's work in detail and it extends your liability to undetected errors and omissions that may subsequently lead to building failures. Unless you truly intend to perform inspection, with all the depth of detail and inherent liability this entails, do not use the term carelessly. In fact, avoid the words *inspection* and *supervision* in your contract, your correspondence and other documentation. You should also include a well-worded definition of what construction observation does and does not include, in either the workscope or definitions section of your agreement.

Keep comprehensive records of what is observed on your jobsite visits. Your firm should establish a field manual with proper procedures; then make sure that field personnel follow those procedures when performing construction observation. Document each visit, using logs, reports and photographs. Many firms make videotapes to document their site observation. Still others have their field people dictate an audio tape — either while walking the site or immediately thereafter — for file purposes.

145

Construction observation is not a job for junior staff, unless accompanied by a senior staff member. In fact, many firms insist that their most experienced professionals conduct project site activities.

Keep in mind that construction observation by the design professional does not relieve the contractor of his or her obligations under the construction contract — particularly for the means and methods of construction and responsibility for jobsite safety. This distinction should be clearly set out in your contract and reflected in the contractor's General Conditions.

Resist the temptation to eliminate construction observation services in exchange for a lower fee. If an owner absolutely refuses your construction observation services, you must obtain very strong contractual protection for claims that arise due to the lack of coordination or the lack of professional interpretation of the construction documents during the construction phase. If the client refuses this protection, consider turning down the project.

No matter how detailed or near perfect you believe your plans to be, they will require some interpretation. By conducting construction observation, you can help make sure that construction is proceeding as it should. To protect your interests and those of your client, it is important to make sure that any needed clarification or interpretation is provided by those best qualified: those who prepared the documents in the first place.

Shop Drawing and Submittal Review

Because of the increasing complexity of construction, the review of shop drawings and submittals often results in claims against design professionals.

Part of the problem is that parties to construction often do not understand that the purpose of your review is to check for conformance with the design concept, not for accuracy or completeness of details or quantities and procedures. Another problem may be that the architect or engineer may not have in place a good system to track shop drawings and submittals from the contractor. As a result, submittals can get lost or "fall between the cracks." Then, too, if the design professional has not established — and adhered to and insisted the contractor adhere to — a strict schedule of submittal, some contractors will overwhelm the design professional with countless shop drawings to review at the last minute. Any of the above situations will lead to delays in processing submittals that can cause major problems for the contractors and, in turn, for the design professionals. Because specifications usually require that the contractor wait to order materials until after the shop drawings have been reviewed, any delay in processing shop drawings may affect the contractor's scheduling and, therefore, can result in a claim for extra costs.

Sometimes design professionals are tempted to review submittals they do not need to see or review aspects of the drawings that should remain the responsibility of the contractor. This may involve the design firm unnecessarily in delay or negligence claims.

Problems also arise when the review task is assigned to personnel who are not the best qualified for the job. Shop drawing and submittal review should not be given to the least experienced in your firm. In fact, many firms believe the project manager should review submittals. Some also have a second member of their firm double check the review before it is returned to the contractor. Remember, there is no substitute for careful and complete shop drawing review.

To manage shop drawings and submittals more efficiently:

- Make certain your contract clearly defines your duties and purpose in reviewing submittals, as well as what you will not be responsible for (such as quantities and dimensions, or the techniques of construction). Likewise, make sure that the General Conditions of the contractor's contract with the owner makes clear the purpose of your submittal review.

- Identify ahead of time the submittals you will review. Request a schedule of those submittals from the contractor — and insist the contractor adheres to it. Never review submittals that concern the actual means, methods or sequences of construction. These are the contractor's responsibility.

- If you receive shop drawings or submittals you did not request, stamp them "Not Required for Review" and return them to the contractor.

- Don't accept submittals directly from a subcontractor or vendor, and reject shop drawings or samples you believe have not been properly reviewed by the contractor prior to transmittal. Return such submittals at once to the contractor with a letter of explanation and ask that the appropriate steps required in the contractor's contract be taken before you review them.

- Date stamp each submittal as soon as it is received and log it in. (See *Exhibit 17* for a sample shop drawing log.) Instruct employees who receive and record the submittals to deliver them to the proper person immediately after logging them in.

- Designate the maximum number of working days you need to process submittals and don't exceed that maximum. Assign a responsible employee to maintain a tickler file of all submittals being processed. Make this person responsible for follow-up every day (or at appropriate intervals) until the shop drawings leave the office. If problems prevent completion of the review within the designated period, notify the project manager.

- Use a shop drawing checklist. (See *Exhibit 18* for a page from one firm's checklist.)

- Use a shop drawing stamp to indicate you have reviewed the submittals. To prevent misunderstandings of the intent in your review, choose the language on your stamp carefully. The wording should reflect your contract workscope concerning the purpose of your review. As noted in Chapter Two, many people

Exhibit 17   Shop Drawing Log

Shop Drawing Log

Expert & Sage, Inc.
Consulting Engineers
3424 Michigan Avenue
Chicago, Il 60654

Category: _____

Log-In Date	Req'd Log-Out	Trans No.	Shop Drawing Title	Sent to Cnsltnt	Rec'd From Cnsltnt	File No.	Log-Out Date	Time Elapsed

Exhibit 18 Shop Drawing Checklist

Shop Drawing Checklist

Expert & Sage, Inc.
Consulting Engineers
3424 Michigan Avenue
Chicago, IL 60654

Project: *Conglomerate Towers*
Client: *Ace and Associates*
Project Location: _____
Date: _____

Submittal Description (Manufacturer, etc.):
Heating Water Pumps,
Primary and Secondary
(Apex System)

General Items	1st Checker	2nd Checker
1. Item manufacturer submitted was one specified	*YES* HPM	✓ LDC
2. Item manufacturer submitted a substitution not specified	*NO* HPM	✓ LDC
3. Item mode/type submitted is that specified	*YES* HPM	✓ LDC
4. Item submitted has performance (capacity) specified	*YES* HPM	✓ LDC
5. Item motor electrical data submitted matches electrical service to motors	*YES* HPM	✓ LDC
6. Item motor type matches that specified	*YES* HPM	✓ LDC
7. Item pressure ratings match specified	*YES* HPM	✓ LDC
8. ASME codes and rating match specified	*NOT REQUIRED* HPM	✓ LDC
9. Item optional accessories submitted match those specified	*YES* HPM	✓ LDC
10. Specified certifications of testing submitted	*YES* HPM	✓ LDC

outside the construction industry assume *approved* means "unqualified acceptance." Some firms seek to solve this problem by using phrases such as *no exceptions taken, furnish as submitted* or, when modifications are needed, *furnish as corrected* or *revise and resubmit* on their shop drawing stamp. Regardless of the words you decide to use on your stamp, they are no substitute for a careful review of the submittals by qualified checkers. (See *Exhibit 19* for two sample shop drawing stamps.) It is a good idea to review your stamp, compare it with the samples and, if necessary, develop appropriate wording with your attorney.

Make certain the General Conditions of the contractor's contract provide that, although some errors may be overlooked in your review, this does not grant the contractor permission to proceed knowingly in error, and that regardless of *any* information contained in the shop drawings, the requirements of the contract documents are not waived or superseded in any way by the shop drawing review. Furthermore, never use the shop drawing review to change the requirements of the contract documents. Use other means (such as change orders) to alter the contractual obligations of the contractor.

Working With Contractors

Your firm's contacts with contractors are of critical importance. Whether you use specially designated employees to handle all field review or you require each of your project managers to conduct construction observation on his or her own projects, personnel who go into the field should be required to follow established procedures. These procedures, when prepared by personnel with substantial experience on the project site, can reduce your exposure to claims significantly.

Exhibit 19 Shop Drawing Stamps

<table>
<tr><td>

☐ Reviewed   ☐ Furnish as Corrected

☐ Rejected   ☐ Revise and Resubmit

☐ Submit Specific Item

This review is only for general conformance with the design concept of the project and general compliance with the information given in the Contract Documents. Corrections or comments made on the shop drawings during this review do not relieve contractor from compliance with the requirements of the plans and specifications. Approval of a specific item shall not include approval of an assembly of which the item is a component. Contractor is responsible for: dimensions to be confirmed and correlated at the jobsite; information that pertains solely to the fabrication processes or to the means, methods, techniques, sequences and procedures of construction; coordination of his or her Work with that of all other trades; and for performing all work in a safe and satisfactory manner.

{Name of Design Professional Firm}

Date _____ By _____

</td><td>

☐ Approved   ☐ Approved as Corrected

☐ Rejected   ☐ Revise and Resubmit

☐ Submit Specific Item

This review is only for general conformance with the design concept of the project and general compliance with the information given in the Contract Documents. Corrections or comments made on the shop drawings during this review do not relieve contractor from compliance with the requirements of the plans and specifications. Approval of a specific item shall not include approval of an assembly of which the item is a component. Contractor is responsible for: dimensions to be confirmed and correlated at the jobsite; information that pertains solely to the fabrication processes or to the means, methods, techniques, sequences and procedures of construction; coordination of the Work of all trades; and for performing all work in a safe and satisfactory manner.

{Name of Design Professional Firm}

Date _____ By _____

</td></tr>
</table>

Some special problem areas that should be addressed in your procedures are:

- **Arguing** — Statements made in anger inevitably increase hostility and reduce the level of cooperation between the parties involved. Getting angry interferes with your ability to work together in the future. Discussion of problems should be postponed until issues can be discussed rationally.

- **Trading** — Never induce a contractor to perform extra work — made necessary by an omission or error in the drawings and specifications — by allowing the contractor, in return, to omit another specified requirement. This practice is unethical and the owner suffers a disservice by such bargaining.

- **The gratuitous undertaking** — Don't let your field personnel give the contractor more information than required. This "volunteered" sharing of the contractor's problem-solving task may lead to a sharing of liability for the contractor's performance. The normal function of your employees does not include advising about the actions or directing of the contractor or his or her workers in any way. Although a cooperative relationship between the contractor and your employees is always desirable, the present legal climate demands that you stick to your own defined tasks during the construction process.

153

You may eliminate some of the problems mentioned above by stipulating that your firm's construction review personnel have no authority to make changes to the contract documents, and that changes, without exception, must be channeled through the client.

Some design firms require the general contractor to acknowledge in writing that the design professional's field representative has no power to authorize changes. A copy of the signed letter is sent to the client. Some firms feel that this procedure has saved them thousands of dollars by avoiding misunderstandings.

Summary

- The success of your practice rests on the commitment to quality at every level of your firm. This philosophy must be driven by your firm's principals, who should urge employees to strive to do the job right the first time.

- The potential for errors and omissions is always present in design work. The prudent design professional, therefore, provides himself or herself with "safety nets" to make sure mistakes are caught and corrected before they cause major difficulties.

- Document all your design decisions and recommendations, as well as the decisions of others.

- Give special attention to the materials and products you specify.

- Make certain your client understands that errors *will* occur, and that you will work together to correct them as quickly and inexpensively as possible.

- Have in place a procedure for responding to requests for clarification from bidders during the bid phase.

- Ensure that your scope of services allows you to perform construction phase services, including construction observation. It is the best way to assure yourself that the project is being built in general conformance with the contract documents and according to design concept.

- Make sure the contractor and your client understand your duties and the purpose behind your review of shop drawings and submittals. Have in place strict schedules and procedures that both you and the contractor are expected to follow.

PROFESSIONAL LIABILITY INSURANCE

A professional liability insurance policy may seem intimidating at first glance. Nevertheless, we highly recommend that you carefully read yours. Your insurance coverage is an important part of your overall risk management strategy. You need to understand the protection you have and, if you hope to reduce your professional liability loss exposure, you must learn to recognize which of your professional activities are not or cannot be insured. You can use this knowledge to choose your projects and clients more carefully, to define the services you will perform or not perform, and to persuade the other parties in negotiations to accept reasonable provisions in your contracts. Just as important, you need to be able to recognize insurance requirements from your client that are impossible or too costly to meet.

An agent or broker can help you understand a great deal about insurance. Find one who specializes in serving design professionals and take advantage of his or her expertise. It costs no more to use a knowledgeable broker who is capable of properly analyzing your coverage needs and problems than to use an amateur. He or she will help you compare differences in the coverages offered and identify the best insurance program available. A skilled broker's analysis could help you avoid decisions that might cost you dearly in the long run. A broker can also assist you in evaluating your appetite for risk and the available means for transferring, funding and retaining risk. Together, you can decide whether your deductible is appropriate, whether you need higher (or lower) limits, whether there are alternatives to standard insurance policies that will better fit your financial situation and whether you need other types of coverages.

Selecting a Broker

If you are a DPIC insured, you already have a good agent or broker who specializes in professional liability insurance for design professionals. If you don't work with DPIC's carefully chosen network of independent specialists, however, you will need to invest time and energy in finding a broker who can respond to your needs.

Talk to your colleagues and the local chapter of your professional society and get the names of those agents or brokers who write coverage for other design professionals. Then, spend some time with at least two of the specialists recommended and discuss your practice with them. Find out about the services they offer to their insureds. Do they review client contracts and provide liability education programs? With which professional liability insurance companies do they do business? Discuss their practice, too — their other insureds, their support staff, their backgrounds.

It is important to find someone who will take the time to learn about your practice. Your insurance protection and liability exposures are too important to trust to less than the best professional you can find. Remember, in choosing a broker, you are also choosing an advisor, and, it is hoped, a dedicated and committed advocate for you and your profession.

Key Insurance Concepts

It's important to understand the language in your policy. That doesn't mean you have to become an insurance expert. At the very least, though, you should understand three key elements of your coverage: *claims-made policies, prior acts coverage* and *expense within limits.*

Claims-Made Policies

Professional liability insurance for design professionals is written on policy forms called *claims-made* or *claims-made and reported* policies. These policies cover only those claims made against you *and* reported to the insurance company during the policy term and any extended reporting periods.

All claims-made policies are alike in that they cover claims reported to the insurance company during the policy period. However, they sometimes differ in their actual definition of what constitutes a "claim" and triggers the policy. Some policies define a claim as *knowledge of a circumstance* that could reasonably be expected to lead to a demand for money or services. Other, more narrow policies define a claim as a *demand for money and services.* This second definition means that even though you know someone is likely to demand money or services from you in connection with problems on a project you have worked on, it is not considered a claim until the demand is actually made.

159

If your policy has the second, more narrow, definition of a claim, it is best *not* to switch insurance companies if you know of any circumstances that could lead to a claim. If you do switch, you could lose insurance coverage for that incident, because any new insurer will exclude "situations of which you have knowledge" that could result in a claim. You should wait to make any change of insurer until either the circumstances develop into a claim, or you can safely conclude they will not.

Prior Acts Coverage

Professional liability policies cover claims arising from negligent acts, errors or omissions committed after a specific date, called the *retroactive date*. This retroactive date may be the date on which you first purchased and have since maintained continuous coverage, the inception date of your firm, or some other date offered by your insurer. Coverage for the services you have performed since your retroactive date up to the present is called *prior acts coverage*. A claim involving your negligent acts, errors or omissions prior to the retroactive date will not be covered.

Typically, most claims arise within two to three years after substantial completion of a project. Since claims arising before construction is completed are less likely, the most valuable part of your coverage is for prior acts.

Some claims-made policies provide an *extended reporting period* that allows a specified interval — 60 days, for example — for reporting claims after the expiration of the policy if such claims are for negligent acts, errors or omissions committed during the period covered by the policy.

Policies do differ. Consult with your broker if you have any questions at all about your coverage. In general, it is essential that you keep your professional liability insurance continuously in force so you can maintain coverage for your current projects as well as prior acts coverage for those you've worked on since your retroactive date. (See *Exhibit 20*.)

Expense Within Limits

The effort to defend against claims costs money — sometimes lots of money. *Expense within limits* is a provision of professional liability policies that means the limit of liability stated in your policy — the dollar amount available to pay claims — will be reduced by the cost of defense and other *allocated claims expenses* associated with those claims. This policy provision is important because it means that your policy limit could be depleted by a single claim that has substantial defense costs. It is also the reason that effective claims management by your insurer and attorney to avoid unnecessary legal expense is so crucial to your firm. Depleted limits of coverage could mean a judgment or settlement in excess of the remaining limit, which then becomes your personal financial responsibility.

The Practice Policy

Exhibit 21 shows the declarations page of an insurance policy as well as the index to its contents. As you review your policy, ask yourself the following questions:

What Is Insured?

The *insuring agreement* specifies the terms under which the company will insure (or pay on behalf of) you, the *named insured*. Most insurance companies will pay because of "error, omission or negligent act," committed by you. This is called the *indemnity* portion of your policy. It means the insurance company will be at risk on your behalf for damages and expenses that arise out of your negligent professional performance, subject to the

Exhibit 20 Insurance Policy Timeline

Date Allegedly Faulty
Service Rendered

Date Claim is Made
Against Firm and
Reported to Carrier

2000

NO COVERAGE

1999 ← Z

Firm Continues to "Go Bare"

1998

C →

1997

Expiration of Policy

COVERAGE

1996 ← Y

Policy Year 3

B →

Policy Year 2   1995 ← X

Policy Year 1   1994

Firm First Purchases
Professional Liability
Insurance (Retroactive Date)

1993

NO COVERAGE

1992

A →

1991

Firm Operates "Bare"
(Without Coverage)

Firm is Established   1990

For coverage to apply, the claim must be made during the active term of a policy and must be based upon services rendered after the retroactive date stated in the policy. For example:

Situation One: Claim is made at X alleging error was made at A. No coverage. Claim was made for an act performed prior to the Retroactive Date in the policy.

Situation Two: Claim is made at Y for alleged omission at B. Coverage would apply, subject to limits and deductible for Policy Year Three.

Situation Three: Claim is made at Z for a negligent act performed at B. No coverage. Claim was made after expiration of coverage under Policy Year Three.

Situation Four: Claim is made at Z for a negligent act at C. No coverage. Both the alleged acts and the claim occurred after the expiration of the last year of coverage.

Exhibit 21 Professional Liability Insurance Policy

Index To Policy Provisions

The contents of your policy can be found quickly by reference to the pages shown in this index. Read your policy carefully as most items interrelate with other items.

I. **Insuring Agreements**

    A. What We Insure
    B. What We Do Not Insure
        1. Contracts
        2. Property
        3. Care-Custody-Control
        4. Workers Compensation
        5. Employers' Liability
        6. Punitive Damages
        7. Fraud and Dishonesty
        8. Cost/Quantity Estimates
        9. Computers
        10. Customary Services
        11. Other Coverage
        12. Insurance
        13. Design/Build
        14. Environmental Damage
        15. Asbestos
        16. Joint Venture
        17. ERISA
    C. Who Is An Insured
    D. Where and When We Insure

II. **Limits of Insurance**

    A. Limit
    B. Aggregate
    C. Multiple Claims
    D. Excess of Deductible
    E. Deductible

III. **Definitions Used In This Policy**

    A. Aggregate
    B. Allocated Claims Expenses
    C. Claim
    D. Claims Made
    E. Contract
    F. Damages
    G. Personal Injury
    H. Property Damage

IV. **Conditions Affecting This Insurance**

    A. Duties In the Event of Claim or Suit
    B. Settlement
    C. Legal Action Against Us
    D. Transfer of Rights of Recovery Against Others To Us
    E. Other Insurance
    F. Inspections and Surveys
    G. Examinations of Your Books and Records
    H. Premium Audit
    I. Transfer of Your Rights and Duties
    J. Premiums
    K. Cancellation
    L. Changes
    M. Bankruptcy

163

Exhibit 21 Professional Liability Insurance Policy (continued)

Declarations
PROFESSIONAL LIABILITY
POLICY

40 Design Professionals Insurance Company
P.O. Drawer DPIC • Monterey, CA 93940

POLICY NUMBER
CODE NO.

Coverage is provided in the Company designated by Number
A Stock Insurance Company and Member of Orion Capital Companies
(herein called the Company)

SPECIMEN

Item 1 **NAMED INSURED:**

Item 2 **MAILING ADDRESS:**

Item 3 **NAMED INSURED IS:** ☐ Individual ☐ Partnership ☐ Corporation ☐ Joint Venture

Item 4 **POLICY PERIOD:** Effective Date: _____ Expiration Date: _____
(12:01 a.m. Local Time at the Above Mailing Address)

Item 5 **LIMITS OF INSURANCE:** EACH CLAIM   AGGREGATE   PREMIUM

Professional Liability $ _____ / $ _____
Shared Expense   See Endorsement $ _____
Education Program Credits   See Endorsement $ _____
L.O.L. Credits   See Endorsement $ _____
Special Coverage   See Endorsement $ _____
Other   See Endorsement $ _____
    $ _____
    $ _____
    Sub-Total $ _____

Item 6 **TOTAL PREMIUM** $ _____

Item 7 **DEDUCTIBLE:** $ _____ Each Claim $ _____

Item 8 **NOTICE OF "CLAIMS-MADE AND REPORTED" POLICY:**
Professional Liability coverage is on a "claims-made and reported basis." Coverage applies only to those "claims" that are first reported to the Company during the policy period.

Item 9 **NOTICE OF EXPENSE WITHIN THE LIMITS:**
Professional Liability Coverage contains a provision that: (a) reduces the limits of insurance stated in the policy by the costs of "allocated claims expenses" and/or (b) permits "allocated claims expenses" to be applied against the deductible or retention amount, if any.

Item 10 **RETROACTIVE DATE:** _____

Item 11 The policy consists of this Declaration Page, Jacket, Insuring Agreement and Endorsements listed here:

8000-2 (2/91):
7023-0 (1/91):

PLEASE READ THE POLICY CAREFULLY AND DISCUSS THIS COVERAGE WITH THE INSURANCE AGENT OR BROKER DESIGNATED BELOW.

Agent: _____   **Date Issued:** _____

Countersigned by: _____

Countersigned at: _____

other terms and conditions of the policy. In addition, the insurance company has a *duty to defend* you for claims under your policy; that is, to provide you with a qualified attorney until the policy limits are exhausted.

What Is Not Insured?

The *exclusions* section of a professional liability policy generally starts by stating, "This insurance does not apply to: . . . ." and is followed by a list of what the insurer does not intend to cover. This limits the coverage provided in the insuring agreement. Each insurance company's list of exclusions is different and should be studied carefully. Some of the exclusions may be removed if special coverage is purchased; that is, by negotiating with your insurance company, you may be able to have an *endorsement* (an amendment) added to your professional liability policy that deletes certain exclusions — in other words, puts the coverage back in force.

There are several reasons why insurance companies use exclusions. First, your professional liability carrier does not intend to cover something that is insured under a different policy. Workers compensation, auto liability and physical damage, general liability and property insurance are examples of coverages that are provided by other policies and excluded by the typical professional liability form.

You may encounter these different policies
in connection with your practice:

- **Auto Liability** — Provides coverage for losses caused by injuries to persons and legal liability imposed on the insured for such injury or for damage to property.

- **Builder's Risk** — Normally carried by a contractor or owner. Also termed All Risk or Course of Construction; intended to cover both the labor and materials necessary to rebuild in the event of destruction in mid-construction.

- **General Liability** — Provides coverage for legal liability to third parties that are not a result of a design professional's professional acts, errors or omissions. Commonly applies to exposure created by the premises and a firm's operations.

- **Non-Owned Auto Insurance** — Provides coverage for liability and property damage claims which may be caused by automobiles not owned or hired by the firm.

- **Professional Liability Insurance** — Formerly called errors and omissions insurance. Protects the design professional against claims arising from negligent errors, acts or omissions in the performance of his or her professional services.

- **Project Insurance** — Provides project-specific professional liability coverage for one or all members of a design team on a given project.

- **Valuable Papers Coverage** — Covers the cost of replacing or redrawing documents lost due to fire, water damage or other specified perils.

- **Workers Compensation** — Required by state law for all employers. Provides benefits for medical costs and lost wages caused by work-connected illness or injury.

Second, insurers can't possibly charge enough to cover certain kinds of extreme risks, such as work involving nuclear energy or hazards involving any type of asbestos product.

Third, professional liability insurance underwriters can't insure activities for which they are unable to measure and quantify risk. This includes activities that are not normally part of the standard design professional services — the assumption of another party's liability by contract, for instance, or the sale of computer software.

Fourth, insurers will not cover claims when doing so would be "contrary to public policy." In other words, if you do something illegal, good public policy says there should not be insurance to protect you. This usually includes claims for dishonest, fraudulent, or criminal acts and claims for punitive damages.

It is important to review your policy exclusions thoroughly. This portion of a professional liability insurance policy has a tremendous impact on the effectiveness of your insurance. Keep in mind, too, that not all limitations to your coverage are contained in the exclusions section. Some conditions in the policy (such as your obligation to notify your carrier of a claim) and some policy definitions (the varying definitions of *damages*, for example) may also directly or indirectly limit your coverage.

Who Is Insured?

The *named insured* on the policy can be an individual, a partnership, a joint venture or a corporation. Within such entities, the partners, executive officers and directors may also be insureds, as may be all your employees while they are performing professional services within the scope of their employment. Coverage for former principals or employees is provided under some policies but must be negotiated in others. You should double check to see that your policy provides the coverage you want for former staff members.

167

Where Are You Insured?

While all U.S. professional liability insurance policies apply to claims brought in the United States, its territories and Canada, some policies also provide (or can be endorsed to provide) worldwide coverage regardless of where a suit is brought. If you have projects in other countries, you need to evaluate your exposure to determine how broad your foreign coverage should be and negotiate for that coverage.

What Are the Policy Limits?

All professional liability policies have an *aggregate* limit of coverage. An aggregate limit is the maximum amount an insurance company will pay on your behalf for all damages, judgments or settlements — including claims expenses — for *all claim*s made and reported during the policy term and any extended reporting period. It doesn't matter how many claims are made in one policy period — one or ten — the aggregate limit is the total the insurer is obligated to pay.

Some insurers offer *split limits* policies. The insured can select a per claim limit as the maximum payable for any one claim and an aggregate limit as the maximum payable for all claims in a policy period. These policies allow firms to cap the amount they are liable for in any one claim and thus limit just how deep their "deep pockets" will be.

When selecting the policy limits for your firm, it is important to think about the number of projects that will be covered. Remember, past projects could still develop problems. Consider, too, your firm's use of subconsultants — which means more exposure to vicarious liability — and projects with high third-party risk. Your agent or broker will help you review these factors.

What Is the Deductible?

The limits on the policy apply in excess of your policy deductible, which is a *per claim* deductible as stated on the policy. For example, if you have a limit of $500,000, a deductible of $10,000 and one claim during the policy period, the insurance will pay up to $500,000 after you fulfill your $10,000 deductible obligation. If you have two or more separate claims, you are responsible for a $10,000 deductible on each claim.

Almost half of the claims against architects and engineers are resolved without indemnity payments, that is, without a judgment or settlement against them. But it might cost their entire deductible in legal expenses just to resolve the matter.

Just as you decide on a deductible amount, you can also choose ways to protect that deductible. Some professional liability insurers offer optional programs — for a price — that let you reserve your deductible for indemnity payments. Look for programs in which the insurer will pay every penny of defense costs up to the policy limit. You would pay the deductible only if there is a judgment or settlement against you.

Some insurers also offer programs in which they share in paying the costs of defense. Under this kind of program, the insurer would pay, say, 80 percent of the expenses and you would pay 20 percent.

Important Conditions That Affect Your Insurance

You should be aware of other parts of your professional liability policy. For instance, your policy requires that you give prompt notice of any claim or lawsuit. Further, you must cooperate with your insurance carrier in the investigation, settlement and defense of the claim or suit. Any expenses you incur related to the defense of a suit (such as costs for your own time, travel

169

or photocopying) are not usually recoverable under the policy or chargeable to the deductible.

Your policy may stipulate that your professional liability insurer cannot settle any claim without your written consent. If, however, you refuse to consent to any settlement recommended by your carrier and you elect to contest the claim or to continue litigation, the insurance carrier's obligation for that claim usually will not exceed the amount for which the claim could have been settled.

If there is any other valid or collectible insurance available for any claim, your professional liability carrier will usually not be obligated to pay until and unless the other coverage is exhausted.

Insurance Pricing

Professional liability insurance for design professionals is especially difficult to quantify and price because of the differences in firm practices, the sizes of projects undertaken, the uncertainties of the legal system (and how it will judge a specific situation), interest rates and the future availability and cost of reinsurance (the insurance that backs up the primary coverage you receive from your insurer).

Still, established companies that insure design professionals have become increasingly sophisticated in analyzing the risk elements involved. Every insurance company employs underwriters, whose job it is to assess the risks your firm represents and properly price those risks. They begin by taking your billings and multiplying them by an established rate to arrive at a base premium. This base premium is then adjusted up or down depending on factors that influence your risk.

For example, if you use insured subconsultants, you may pay less because you are less likely to become a "deep pocket" in the event your subconsultant causes a claim. If you are involved in a low-risk discipline (surveying or landscape design) instead of a high-risk discipline (structural engineering), you may pay less. If you practice in rural areas of the Midwest rather than in California or New York, you may pay less (because of the more favorable legal climate). If you design industrial/commercial buildings, provide interior design services or do a lot of preliminary studies or reports, you may pay less than those who design very risky projects such as condominiums and bridges. If, in the underwriter's judgment and based on the information available, your firm is very well managed, you may pay less. Finally, if you have had better claims experience than typical firms of your size and discipline, you may also pay less.

Clearly, there are ways you can influence what you pay for insurance. A specialized agent or broker can work with you to reduce your risk and therefore your premiums.

Project Professional Liability Insurance

Your annual practice policy applies to all claims made against your firm that arise out of your professional practice subject to any policy provisions. In contrast, a *project professional liability policy*, like DPIC's TeamCover, applies to one specific project.

A project policy applies to claims made during the design and construction phase, plus a preselected *reporting period* following substantial completion of the project. The length of the discovery period can be specifically tailored to each project — up to five years after construction has ended.

Using a project policy offers many advantages to the design professional team:

- The professional liability premium has a guaranteed rate and is calculated specifically for one project, making it simple to isolate the costs and pass them directly to the owner. In fact, the owner will often agree to pay the premium.

- The design professional firm's annual practice policy premium is typically reduced because the fees for the project policy are removed from the practice policy premium calculation.

- In most instances, all the design professionals on a project are covered, even those subconsultants who are otherwise uninsured or underinsured. This drastically reduces the risks of *vicarious liability* (exposure for another party's — e.g., a subconsultant's — work) and cross complaints from other team members.

- A project policy is non-cancelable under most circumstances. Unless there's been a breach in policy conditions, a misrepresentation on the application or nonpayment of premium, coverage is guaranteed to remain in force for the entire policy period selected. This eliminates concerns about coverage being unavailable in the future.

- Because there is a single point of claims responsibility (one insurer) for the project, the focus is on problem solving, not "finger pointing," among members of the design team in order to resolve disputes.

- Claims paid under a project policy will not affect the design professional's claims history. The design professional's practice policy rate will not be increased just because there were claims under a project policy.

Project insurance also provides the project owner with tangible benefits. First, the policy limits are dedicated to the project and are not subject to depletion by claims from other projects. Second, coverage is assured in force for a reasonable period after substantial completion. Third, since all members of the design team are usually insured under the project policy, solving problems is simplified, resulting in a smoother running project.

There has been an increased interest in project policies as a means of dealing equitably with the requirements of owners and design professionals for dependable, effective protection. Your specialized agent or broker can provide you with more information on project professional liability insurance for your projects.

178

Summary

- Insurance may appear complicated, but your agent and your insurance company are available to help you understand how it works.

- It is important to understand the extent and limits of your coverage. Take the time to learn certain basic concepts about professional liability insurance and then review your own policy.

- A number of factors determines the price of your professional liability insurance, such as your discipline, your geographic location, your choice of projects and your claims history.

- A project policy offers many advantages to the design team and the owner of a project. It can reduce your risk and that of your client, is generally non-cancelable, and can result in fewer disputes on the project.

175

WHERE TO GET HELP

It's an old truism that the wise person may not know all the answers but knows where to find them. After reading this far, you probably have some questions about applying the lessons in this manual to your everyday practice. You don't need to try to figure it out alone, though. There are many professionals who are well-equipped to help you answer those questions.

Legal Counsel

All firms, large and small, need a competent individual to consult on legal matters. Make sure you have an attorney on tap who understands the construction industry and your discipline in particular.

The two types of attorneys most often used by design professionals are trial lawyers and business attorneys. One person is rarely skilled in both disciplines, but a firm that specializes in the design professional field can often offer you both. You should identify trial attorneys who understand dispute resolution methods as well as litigation. You should also search carefully for a "general practitioner" specialized in your field who can help you prevent claims and legal problems. This type of lawyer can help you review and negotiate contracts, examine your in-house loss prevention measures and advise you on how to keep problems from developing into disputes.

A Legal Checkup

Every architectural or engineering firm should have an attorney perform a thorough review of its contracts and practices, as well as a legal review after any significant change in operations. The assignment should be to review and make recommendations about:

- Your firm's professional agreements
- Your firm's documentation and internal record keeping procedures
- Your firm's negotiating practices on contracts, including "best case" preferred wording, fall-back positions and Deal Breaker issues for a given project (See Chapter 4, page 86)
- Personnel, corporate and partnership agreements, ownership transition plans, multi-state practices, licensing and other matters

The question of the fee for this consultation should be raised with the attorney prior to the meeting, as the time and expense involved will vary widely among firms. Keep in mind that the fee you pay will probably save you time and money in the long run.

Unfortunately, the need for legal advice won't go away just because you've had a comprehensive review. You will need to be able to call your attorney at a moment's notice for help on a tough contract or in a situation requiring legal expertise. The important thing is to establish a relationship with a good attorney *before* you need him or her. If a problem arises, you should have someone to call who knows you and your firm.

Finding an Attorney

In selecting an attorney, use the same methodology you want clients to use when searching for an architectural or engineering firm: Ask other design professionals, your professional society and your professional liability insurance carrier and broker for the names of at least two or three attorneys who have experience in your field. The law firm you select must be experienced in working with design professionals and in the type of work you want done.

Invite each recommended lawyer to meet with you to talk about his or her suggestions for your firm. Before you set up this meeting, ask if there will be a fee. Many attorneys consider such a meeting part of their marketing program and may not bill you for it unless you discuss a specific case or problem with them.

Don't be afraid to ask how much the attorney charges. Generally, attorneys are not reluctant to let you know the basis of their fees. Keep in mind, however, that hourly rates are only one factor to consider. Expertise —

179

efficiency in dealing with a particular area of law — is more important. A low-fee attorney might take twice as long as a more expensive "specialist" to do the same work.

You'll also want to ask if or how the attorney charges for travel time. This will be important if the attorney has to travel to a remote site or some other city on your behalf.

Be sure to ask the attorney for the names of several design professionals for whom he or she has worked and whom you may call for references. If the attorney is a good one, he or she will respect you for your thoroughness and — by following up with the references — you gain further insight into his or her competence.

Once you have selected an attorney, be cooperative and open. He or she can't be expected to be an instant expert in your particular practice, but should be a fast learner. You may have to provide details and confidential information about your problems, but your attorney needs to be fully informed to help you. You are, of course, protected by attorney-client privilege; what you disclose usually cannot be revealed by discovery procedures in litigation.

Other Sources of Advice

In addition to attorneys, you will probably want to take advantage of the many other resources available. These include insurance experts, business management consultants, professional association services, and do-it-yourself books and seminars. (One resource is *The Contract Guide: DPIC's Risk Management Handbook for Architects and Engineers.*)

Hiring a Staff Attorney

If your firm is large — with billings of several million in fees — and has many and varied prime contractual relationships, you may want to consider adding an attorney to your staff. If your firm is self-insured, has very large deductibles or pays significant amounts in legal retainer fees, you should consider this option. Even in the largest and most sophisticated firms, there is still great debate on whether to have in-house legal staff, outside counsel or a combination of both. If you are seriously considering hiring an attorney for your staff, you should talk to the management of several design firms your size with in-house attorneys. Talk to their attorneys, if possible. Also discuss the pros and cons of having a staff attorney with your current outside counsel. Make your decision only after you have looked at all aspects of the matter.

Your Insurance Company

Some insurance companies simply provide you with an insurance policy. Insurers with an ongoing commitment to design professionals, however, will go much further in helping you improve your practice and lessen your risk. They will provide newsletters and other materials to help improve your practice. They will be active with the professional societies and knowledgeable about the legislative affairs in your state. In addition, their underwriters, claims staff and legal counsel will be available to you for questions and problem resolution. Good insurance companies want to be of service to you. When you need help, feel free to contact them directly.

Specialized Insurance Agents and Brokers

As we discussed in Chapter Six, insurance agents and brokers who are knowledgeable about the design professions can be worth their weight in gold. These men and women have been trained in the issues that affect design professionals and have seen first-hand how design professionals get into trouble and how these situations are resolved. They offer you the benefits of this experience as well as their familiarity with the scope and nature of your insurance coverage.

Specialized agents and brokers can offer advice and opinions on the insurability of your contracts. They can assist you on insurance matters raised during contract negotiations. They can help you sell your clients on concepts such as limitation of liability and partnering, and on the benefits of using project professional liability insurance. Your agent will also keep you abreast of new options and developments from your insurance company.

Management Consulting Firms

There are many recognized management consulting firms and individuals who specialize in the business problems of design professionals. The efforts of these consultants are directed toward solving organization, staffing and marketing problems. But you will also find their expertise useful in evaluating professional liability and loss prevention practices. Their services can enhance the quality of your services, help you maximize your relationships with clients and reduce your vulnerability to professional liability lawsuits. Ask your peers and your professional society for the names of firms they recommend.

Professional Societies

Professional societies and associations are often overlooked as resources. Yet their assistance is far-ranging and they have a lot more to offer than most design professionals realize. The American Institute of Architects, The American Consulting Engineers Council, ASFE: Professional Firms Practicing in the Geosciences, The Coalition of American Structural Engineers and the National Society of Professional Engineers, for example, have many resources to offer.

By serving as your advocates in Washington, D.C., and in state legislatures throughout the country, these organizations carry out many activities designed to enhance the professions and improve the level of practice and fees. They also act as the watchdogs of the professions, fighting legislation that would put you and your colleagues at a disadvantage.

These organizations provide valuable tools, including literature, standard forms and agreements, and up-to-date information on changes in codes and laws. They can help you gain insight into your business practices through peer review programs. Perhaps best of all, they give you the opportunity — through their meetings and seminars — to talk with other firms who have problems just like yours.

Summary

- Professional liability is a complex business. There is no reason, though, that you should have to know all the answers yourself or have to find them alone.

- Your insurance company, your specialist agent or broker, your attorney, your accountant, your business manager and your professional society or association — all are available to help you have the most profitable, trouble-free practice possible.

ADDITIONAL RESOURCES

To learn more about the subjects we've discussed in this manual, you may want to refer to publications that are available from professional societies, insurance companies, and university and public libraries. We've listed a few below:

Further Reading

ACEC Guidelines to Practice: Alternative Dispute Resolution for Design Professionals. Vol. 1, No. 7, Washington, DC: American Consulting Engineers Council, 1991.

Architect's Handbook of Professional Practice. 11th Ed. Washington, DC: The American Institute of Architects, 1988.

Avoiding and Resolving Disputes During Construction. New York: American Society of Civil Engineers, 1991.

Baynes, K. and Pugh, F. *The Art of the Engineer.* Cambridge, UK: Lutterworth Press, 1981.

Cuff, Dana. *Architecture: The Story of Practice.* Massachusetts: MIT Press, 1991.

Dixon, Sheila A. and Crowell, Richard D. *The Contract Guide: DPIC's Risk Management Handbook for Design Professionals.* Monterey, Ca: DPIC Companies, Inc., 1993.

Effective Business Communication. Chesterton, Laura P., editor. Massachusetts: Houghton Mifflin, 1992.

Engineering Professionalism and Ethics. Schaub, James H. and Pavlovic, Karl, editors. Florida: Kreiger, 1986.

Fisher, Roger and Ury, William and Patton, Bruce. *Getting to Yes: Negotiating Agreement Without Giving In,* 2nd Ed. Massachusetts: Houghton Mifflin, 1991.

Fleury, Robert E. *The Small Business Survival Guide.* Illinois: Sourcebooks Trade, 1991, 1992.

Gellerman, Saul. *Motivation in the Real World.* New York: Dutton, 1992.

Hiring and Firing Book: A Complete Legal Guide for Employers. Merrick, NY: Legal Strategies, Inc., 1993.

Huber, Peter W. *Liability: The Legal Revolution and Its Consequences.* New York: Basic Books, Inc., 1988.

Ingardia, Michael P. and Hill, John F. *CADD Risk Management for Design Firms.* Washington, DC: American Consulting Engineers Council, 1992.

Jablonski, Joseph R. *Implementing TQM: Competing in the Nineties Through Total Quality Management,* 2nd Ed. New Mexico: Technical Management Consortium, 1992.

Larson, M.S., *The Rise of Professionalism.* Berkeley, Ca.: University of California Press, 1977.

The LoL Handbook: A Guide to the Use of Limitation of Liability for Design Professionals, Monterey, Ca.: DPIC Companies, Inc., 1993.

McReynolds, Charles M. *Human Resources Management for Design Firms.* Washington, DC: American Consulting Engineers Council, 1993.

Milling, Bryan E. *The Basics of Finance: Financial Tools for Non-Financial Managers*. Illinois: Sourcebooks Trade, 1991.

Nigro, William T. *Redicheck Interdisciplinary Coordination,* 3rd Ed. The Redicheck Firm, 1992.

Partnering: A Concept for Success. Washington, DC: The Associated General Contractors of America, 1991.

Phillips, Barbara Ashley. *Finding Common Ground: A Field Guide to Mediation*. Halfway, Or.: Hells Canyon Publishing, Inc., 1994.

PLAN Project Representative's Manual. Silver Spring, Md.: Professional Liability Agents Network, 1990.

Preventing and Resolving Construction Disputes. New York: Center for Public Resources, 1991.

A Project Partnering Guide for Design Professionals. Washington, DC: American Consulting Engineers Council and The American Institute of Architects, 1993.

Risk Management/Professional Liability. Washington, DC: American Consulting Engineers Council, 1990.

Tannen, Deborah. *That's Not What I Meant: How Conversation Style Makes or Breaks Your Relations With Others*. New York: William Morrow, 1986.

Trachtenberg, Marven, and Hyman, Isabell. *Architecture: From Prehistory to Post Modernism — The Western Tradition*. New Jersey: Prentice Hall, 1986.

Understanding and Purchasing Professional Liability Insurance. Washington, DC: American Consulting Engineers Council, 1991.

Watkin, David. *A History of Western Architecture*. London, UK: Thames & Hudson, 1986.

187

Woodward, Cynthia A. *Human Resources Management for Design Professionals*. Washington, DC: American Institute of Architects, 1990.

Where to Find Additional Information

American Arbitration Association, 118840 West 51st Street, New York, NY 10020-1203, (212) 484-4000/Fax 307-4387.

American Consulting Engineers Council, 1015 15th Street NW, Washington, DC 20005, (202) 347-7474.

American Institute of Architects, 1735 New York Avenue NW, Washington, DC 20006, (202) 626-7300.

American Management Association, 440 First Street NW, Washington, DC 20001, (202) 347-3092.

American Society of Civil Engineers, 345 East 47th Street, New York, NY 10017-2398, (212) 705-7496.

ASFE: Professional Firms Practicing in the Geosciences, 8811 Colesville Road, Suite G106, Silver Spring, Md. 20910, (301) 565-2733.

Associated General Contractors of America, 1957 E Street NW, Washington, DC 20006, (202) 393-2040.

Center for Public Resources, 366 Madison Avenue, New York, NY 10017, (212) 949-6490.

Coalition of American Structural Engineers, 1015 15th Street NW, Suite 802, Washington, DC 20005, (202) 347-7474.

National Society of Professional Engineers, 1420 King Street,
 Alexandria, Va. 22314-2715, (703) 684-2800.

Professional Liability Agents Network, 3311 Colesville Road, Suite G106,
 Silver Spring, Md. 20910, (301) 589-5642.

Small Business Administration, (800) 827-5722 (Recorded information).

Society of America Value Engineers, 60 Revere Drive, Suite 500,
 Northbrook, Il. 60062, (708) 480-9282.

INDEX

D

Damages 167
Deal Breaker clauses 86, 89-95
Deductible 168-169
Deep pockets 168
Defense and indemnity provisions (*see* Indemnities)
Delays 101, 102, 147
Delivery of plans and specifications 101
Design checklists 127, *exhibit 128*
Design decisions 135-136, 154
Design judgment 116
Design manual 127, 129, *exhibit 130*
Design schedules 101-103, *exhibit 104*, 108, 119, 123
Design without construction phase services 146
Discovery
  period 171
  proceedings 54
Dispute resolution, formal 46-47, *exhibit 48*, 56
  in professional service agreements 47
  methods of
    advisory arbitration 47, 52
    arbitration 49, 51, 52-54
    mediation 44, 47, 49-50
    mediation/arbitration 51-52
    mediation-then-arbitration 52
    minitrial 47, 50-51
    rent-a-judge 54-55
    summary jury trial 55
  range of
    binding 47, 51, 53, 54
    consensual 47, 49, 51
    mandated 47, 50
    nonadjudicative 47
    nonbinding 44, 47, 49, 50, 52, 55
    voluntary 49, 50, 52
  value of 46-47
Dispute review boards 38-39, 58
Disputes
  costs of 33
  cumulative nature of 33
  guidelines for handling 40-44
  prevention of 34-36
  reasons for 31-32, 70-71

Document coordination 136-137
Documentation 24, 26, 28, 43, 135-136, 145
DR (*see* Dispute resolution, formal)
Drawings 126-127, 129, 131
  dimensions on 126-127
  notes on 127
  omissions in 129-131
  relationship to specifications 127
  symbols used in 127
DRBs (*see* Dispute review boards)
Duty to defend 165

E

Education 2, 3, 12, 117
EJCDC 82, 86
Employees (*see* Personnel)
Endorsement 165
Error detection 137-139
Errors and omissions 129, 131, 136, 138, 139, 145, 154
Estimating costs (*see* Opinions of probable cost)
Estimating schedules (*see* Design schedules)
Estimator, professional cost 98
Ethics 6, *exhibit 7*, *exhibit 8*, 9
Excluded services 85-86 (*see also* Scope of services)
Exclusions 165, 166-167
Expense within limits 161
Experimentation 134-135
Extended reporting period 160
Extreme words 13-14

F

Fast-track projects 64
Fee
  collection 69, 74, 103, 105-106, 108, 123
  fairness 74, 123
  negotiation 74-75, 76
Field manual 145
Field representative 153
Field visits 144-145
Final 13, 20
Financial management 3
Foreign coverage 167
Furnish 17, 151

194

195